BIRD BRA

BIRD BRAIN OF BRITAIN

Pit your wits against the experts!

Charles Gallimore and Tim Appleton
Foreword by Bill Oddie

Illustrations by John Cox

CHRISTOPHER HELM
LONDON

Published 2004 by Christopher Helm, an imprint of A & C Black Publishers Ltd.,
37 Soho Square, London W1D 3QZ

ISBN 0-7136-7036-3

A CIP catalogue record for this book is available from the British Library.

www.acblack.com

Printed and bound in Great Britain by Creative Print and Design, Ebbw Vale

10 9 8 7 6 5 4 3 2 1

Cover illustration by Marc Dando

Back photograph (Bird Brain 2000) by Yanina Herridge

CONTENTS

FOREWORD
By Bill Oddie

Originally, Bird Brain of Britain probably had relatively noble intentions. It was conceived as an opportunity for some of the country's most eminent ornithologists to impress the public, whilst indulging a little in the competitiveness inherent in all birdwatchers. The format chosen was similar to that of television's famous Mastermind. Highly qualified contestants sit in the famous black chair and answer questions. Or not. In fact, after barely a couple of rounds of the very first Bird Brain – held in a tiny tent many years ago – it became obvious that its true appeal was more like that of Christians being thrown to the lions. There is nothing an audience enjoys more than witnessing the public humiliation and embarrassment of so-called experts.

Bird Brain was an instant hit, and over the years it has gone from strength to strength – or should that be weakness to weakness? The tent has grown into a huge marquee, the audiences have got bigger, louder and crueller, and the contestants more and more nervous. And yet they still volunteer to be put through this ordeal. Why? Is it charity – or vanity perhaps? You see, you may think you know all the answers 'off stage', but it's not so easy once you get in that chair, with the spotlight on you, the live microphone and the audience staring. Once the timekeeper starts the clock, and the chairman starts rattling through the questions like a robot on speed, it's not surprising that many people go totally blank!

Thus, year after year, Bird Brain exposes distinguished representatives of Britain's major scientific and conservation organisations as apparently having no more knowledge than the birds themselves. Audiences inevitably conclude that our wildlife is in the hands of total ignoramuses, and no doubt the various organisations lose hundreds of members. Never mind, it's 'all in a good cause'. And the good cause is – of course – my personal entertainment. After almost a lifetime of making an idiot of myself on various quizzes and game shows, you can surely appreciate how much I relish seeing other people suffer. I am not sure how much of the experience can be captured in a book – the baying crowd, the perspiring contestants, the scatty scorer and the sadistic chairman – so why not try to reproduce the event in the privacy of your own homes? Invite a bunch of birders over for something innocuous – a slide show on warbler wing formulae perhaps – but instead announce: "Right then, we're going to play Bird Brain! It's my house, so baggsy I'm chairman." And, if they won't let you be chairman, I suggest you say, "Right, I'm not playing then". It worked for me.

Bill Oddie.
March 2004

PREFACE

A Brief History of the British Birdwatching Fair

The British Birdwatching Fair takes place over three days every August at Rutland Water Nature Reserve – part of a huge reservoir in the Midlands managed by Anglian Water. With the support of the Leicestershire and Rutland Wildlife Trust and the RSPB, it has blossomed into a major event on the calendar. Around 16,000 visitors now attend annually, and more than 300 exhibitors from all corners of the world display their products, promoting businesses as diverse as ecotourism, optical equipment, second-hand books and birdfeeders.

All this seems a far cry from the Birdfair's humble beginnings in 1989. Inspired by a local event two years earlier called 'The Wildfowl Bonanza', the idea was hatched by Tim Appleton and Martin Davies over lengthy deliberation in a local pub – appropriately named The Finch's Arms. Their aim was to bring birdwatchers together to celebrate birds and support conservation, and to provide a commercial outlet for the birdwatching industry. Since then, the fair has not only achieved this, but has also proved to be a wonderful shop window for local, national and international conservation organisations. All profits go to BirdLife International and its partners for conservation and since the first project – the 'Stop the Massacre Campaign' in 1989 – more than £1,136,000 has been raised to help save birds and their habitats.

The success of the Birdfair is undoubtedly due to the 'listen and learn' approach that the organisers adopted from the start, and it has always depended upon the contributions of many others. These include the staff and volunteers from Rutland Water Nature Reserve who spend weeks every year preparing the site, and the LRWT and RSPB volunteers who join them during the three days of the fair – thus saving thousands of pounds in service expenditure. Furthermore, the fair would never have been possible without the support of its many generous sponsors, including in focus, Viking Optical, Swarovski Optik, Carl Zeiss, Leica, Bushnell, Jessops, C J Wildbird Foods, Naturetrek and WildSounds. To all these people and organisations, and others too numerous to mention here, we are immensely grateful.

Bird Brain of Britain

In 1992, Tim and Martin decided to try a Mastermind competition at the fair – along the lines of the successful BBC television programme – with Bill Oddie doing the Magnus Magnusson bit. Tim Dixon set the general knowledge questions, while the competitors and their organisations set the specialist questions. The competition proved to be very popular and became a regular event, adopting the title *Bird Brain of Britain* in 1995. Since then, Bill Oddie has continued to terrorise the contestants in most years, with Chris Packham stepping in as Torquemada on a couple of occasions. In recent years Charles Gallimore has taken over from Tim Dixon in setting the questions.

Bird Brain of Britain has always been a light-hearted event. Nobody envisaged it continuing for twelve years, let alone spawning a book. However, a member of the audience during the 2002 event (thank you, whoever you are!) raised this idea, and a book soon began to seem an increasingly good way of raising additional funds for the Birdfair. Unfortunately, the questions for the first eight years had been 'filed' by Tim in a variety of unlikely locations, and it took the best part of two years to unearth them all.

For the sake of a balanced book, the editors have had to do a little tinkering with the original questions and the form in which they first appeared. The specialist questions remain largely unaltered – even in the few cases where one was asked more than once – but a few general knowledge questions that were repeated from year to year have been omitted. Not all questions for every year could be retrieved, so the general knowledge questions have been divided equally to allow 66 questions for each year. This means that some questions have been moved from the year in which they were originally asked. However, the editors have tried to avoid moving year-specific questions.

The editors have also done their best to check the accuracy of the answers, but they make no claims of infallibility and some answers will inevitably be disputed (and for a few there is no right answer). Many have been updated as a result of new knowledge, a change in status or taxonomy, or because the original answer was just plain wrong. Where the change is trivial, no explanation has been given, but an explanation or comment in square brackets has been added to any which have been changed significantly. Various other clarifications for the answers are also placed in square brackets.

There are a couple of other things to note: the vernacular English names of birds have been left largely as they were originally set, without too many Northerns, Commons, Eurasians etc – except where it was felt necessary for clarity. Also, birders are rightly concerned about threats to their beloved birds, and so many questions relate to threat status. To this end, the IUCN's categorisation system has been followed, with initial capitals generally used to denote status.

The format of the book is chronological. Each year's specialist subject and general knowledge questions are preceded by a brief summary of the year's conservation cause. This includes information on how the funds raised were spent, and any recent conservation developments with regard to the year's project. The four contestants (with the names of the organisations they were representing) are listed at the bottom of the 'project page'. An asterisk (*) denotes the winner for each year – the crowned 'Bird Brain of Britain'. The four sets of specialist subjects are presented in the same order as the contestants are listed, so the reader can determine which subjects were chosen by the various 'experts'. The answers are all given at the end, again arranged chronologically. The book concludes with an index of the 48 specialist subjects chosen since the contest began.

Numerous people have assisted by providing up-to-date information to make the answers as accurate as possible, but all errors and omissions are the fault of the editors. The book is meant to be fun, albeit of the kind alluded to in Bill Oddie's Foreword, but we have tried to make it as accurate as possible.

ACKNOWLEDGEMENTS

Reference works, too numerous to mention, have been used to check and update the answers, but special mention should be made of BirdLife International's *Threatened Birds of the World* (2000), which has proved invaluable. Special thanks go to Bill Oddie and Chris Packham for their entertaining inquisitions over the years, and to Tim Dixon, who set the general knowledge questions and collated the specialist subject questions in the beginning, and without whom the quiz would probably have died in infancy. Those noble gladiators, the contestants, who willingly submitted themselves to public ridicule, and who, with their organisations, set nearly all the specialist questions, and indeed many of the general questions, deserve thanks, admiration and sympathy. We are grateful to others who have set questions including Ian Dawson and Martin Henry, and we apologise to others who may have been omitted here. Our thanks go to Martin Davies who has also been the regular scorer (or perhaps that should be irregular scorer), in the quiz, to John Cox, whose cartoons set the right note of levity, to Marc Dando for his delightful cover illustration, and to Paula McCann for designing the book. We are also grateful to those, too numerous to mention individually, who helped to correct and update many of the answers, or gave advice and instruction on the mysteries of word processing. Finally, thanks must be given to the unknown person who asked if a book was planned.

BIRDFAIR 1992
ICPB Spanish Steppes Appeal

The Spanish Steppes are among the largest remaining 'natural' habitats in Europe, comprising a patchwork of dry scrub and rough grassland interspersed with non-intensively farmed cereals, legumes and fallow land. The mosaic of vegetation and the low level of human activity provide rich and diverse feeding and breeding opportunities for birds. More than half the world's population of Great Bustards and up to 75% of the world's population of Little Bustards are to be found in this rich habitat. Severely threatened by increased farming activities, the 1992 Birdfair helped launch the campaign to save the Spanish Steppes, using the £30,000 raised at the Fair. The funds were matched with funding from a European Commission Grant (ACANT, which is now known as Life funding) and used to purchase a steppe reserve in the Aragon region. The Belchite Reserve, covering 239 hectares, was purchased at the end of 1995 and has become, for the BirdLife partner in Spain, SEO, a flagship reserve. It lies in the Ebro Valley and is a stronghold for Dupont's Lark. A visitor centre has been constructed and hides and nature trails laid out. Following extensive lobbying by SEO, subsidies are now paid to farmers in seven provinces containing the Steppes, who farm in an environmentally friendly method. A major victory for the conservation of the Steppes was achieved in November 1994, when the EC agreed to fund a development programme for the Aragon province so long as an irrigation project, which would have damaged the Los Monegros Important Bird Area, was cancelled.

The contestants, under the Chairmanship of Bill Oddie, were:-

Nigel Collar (International Council for Bird Preservation [now BirdLife])
Janet Kear (Wildfowl & Wetlands Trust)
Chris Mead (British Trust for Ornithology)
* Chris Harbard (Royal Society for the Protection of Birds)

SPECIALIST SUBJECTS 1992
Endangered Bird Species

1. Which three breeding British birds are possible candidates for inclusion in the next international Red Data Book?
2. What was unusual about the recent sighting of a Madagascar Pochard?
3. How many of the world's cranes are endangered?
4. What do Lake Skadar (Albania), the Danube Delta (Romania) and Lake Prespa (Greece) have in common?
5. According to ICBP's checklist of threatened birds, how many threatened species are there in Brazil?
6. Where does the Kagu come from?
7. What is the main problem facing the New Zealand Black Stilt?
8. The Corncrake is found breeding in how many European countries?
9. The volcanic islands of Torishima and Minami-Kojima are the only breeding sites for which endangered species of seabird?
10. What alternative English name for the endangered North American Kirtland's Warbler describes its sole breeding habitat?
11. To which island is Abbott's Booby restricted as a breeding bird?
12. What flightless bird, thought to be extinct, was rediscovered in 1948 by G B. Orbell?
13. The Lesser Antillean island of Dominica is home to two endangered Amazon parrots. One is the striking Imperial Parrot. What is the other?
14. Which Ethiopian endemic, collected by an explorer who was killed by an elephant during an expedition to the Rift Valley, was found and described from a collection of birds in the Genoa Museum in 1896, and was not rediscovered until 1941/42 at Arero?
15. What mallee-haunting bird, now perhaps Australia's most endangered species, is being genetically swamped by hybridisation with its Yellow-throated cousin, which is moving into contact through habitat alteration?
16. Which nocturnal wader, not seen since 1900, was rediscovered in 1986?
17. Which bird, known only as a winter visitor to Lake Boraphet in Central Thailand, and first described from ten specimens collected in 1968, has not been reliably reported since 1980?

18. Which countries are thought to have been the range states for Glaucous Macaw?

19. What is the common name of the threatened South American heron *Zebrilus undulatus*?

20. North America has two threatened woodpecker species, one of which, the Ivory-billed, is now considered extinct (in continental America). What is the other?

21. Spain is thought to contain 65% of the world population of which globally threatened species?

22. The last Passenger Pigeon died in Cincinnati Zoo in 1914. What was its name?

23. Which other North American species finally became extinct in the same zoo in the same month?

24. In 1979 a public outcry prevented 8 individuals of a threatened species from being killed by US customs. The birds were given to San Francisco Zoo where they have since bred. Name the species.

25. Henderson Island, home to the threatened Stephen's Lorikeet, came under threat from an unusual problem in 1982, which was averted by the UK Government. What was it?

26. A threatened species was recently rediscovered after an ornithologist played recordings of a similar species to shepherds on an Atlantic island. What was the species?

27. What is the title of the village headman in Cameroon society, who uses the feathers of the threatened Bannerman's Turaco as a symbol of his authority?

28. What wiped out the Stephen Island Wren?

29. Which family of flightless New Zealand birds is now extinct?

30. Which bird's wild population was reduced to one individual in 1992?

31. Which bird species was added to CITES Appendix I at the most recent conference (1992)?

32. Jerdon's Courser was presumed extinct until it was rediscovered in 1986. What characteristic of the species was responsible for its lengthy disappearance?

33. The last Great Auk in the UK was executed for what reason?

34. The Houbara Bustard has declined throughout its range in recent years. When did it last occur in the UK?

35. What fate sometimes befalls Giant Coots?

36. Which island in the Tristan da Cunha group gives its name to the smallest flightless bird?

37. What recent threat is causing problems for the White-headed Duck?

38. The extinct Huia was unique amongst birds. For what reason?
39. What was the record low for female Chatham Island Black Robins before the species began to recover?
40. Which literary prize shares its name with a bird species restricted to Angola?
41. Which of the world's three species of kiwi (in 1992) was considered to be threatened with extinction?
42. Which three globally threatened species occur in the Spanish steppes?

Wildfowl of the World

1. What are the two alternative names for the Plumed Whistling Duck?
2. Name two waterfowl species that might in particular might have an aversion to the Black-headed Duck, also known as the Cuckoo Duck.
3. The female of which species of duck has a strong loral spot?
4. Which duck has the nickname of 'Punk-rocker Duck'?
5. Who saw the first Ring-necked Duck to occur in Britain and Ireland?
6. What do Americans call a 'honker'?

7. What is unusual about the plumage of Screamers?
8. All stifftail ducks are mainly vegetarian except one. Which?
9. How many species of Eider are there?
10. Which species of wildfowl is unique in having a graduated wing moult, and thus not having a period when it is flightless?
11. Which is the world's smallest swan?
12. The breeding grounds of which species of wildfowl were not discovered until June 1938 along the Perry River Delta in the Northwest Territories of Canada?
13. Its nest not recorded in the wild until 1959, what is the only anatid endemic to New Guinea?
14. Which aberrant Australian duck is also known as the Monkey or Oatmeal Duck?
15. Which is the only wildfowl species which indulges in courtship feeding, the male offering food to the female?
16. Which species of wildfowl was only described as a new species as recently as 1981?
17. Which duck of the Mallard group is endemic to Madagascar and Mauritius?
18. All Ruddy Shelducks which have appeared in the UK in recent years are thought to have escaped from captivity. Up to what year were they thought likely to have been wild?
19. Where did the Ruddy Ducks which now threaten to hybridise with Spanish White-headed Ducks originate?
20. What is the world's best known duck?
21. Which globally threatened Pacific wildfowl species was helped by Sir Peter Scott?
22. Which two-tone Asian duck is finally thought to have become extinct in the marshes of Burma (Myanmar)?

Ringing and Migration

1. Where and in what year was the first British bird observatory established?
2. What is the name of the British bird observatory which was founded in 1946 and which closed in 1973?
3. By 1982 over 100,000 Goldcrests had been ringed under the British ringing scheme. How old was the oldest recovered bird?
4. From whom must special permission be obtained to ring Mute Swans on the River Thames?
5. Juveniles of eight British-breeding passerines undergo a

complete moult in summer. Name three.

6. How many primaries do auks have?
7. Where is the eastern race of the Reed Warbler thought to undertake its moult?
8. How many Lanceolated Warblers had been ringed in Britain and Ireland up to the end of 1990 (to the nearest five)?
9. What is unusual about the moult of the Dipper?
10. Apart from the House Martin, which two species of migrant passerine breed in Britain and winter in primary rainforest in Africa?
11. How many visits must be made between May and August in one year to a Constant Effort Ringing Site?
12. What was unusual about the rings with which Jack Miner was marking North American waterfowl before 1914?
13. What technique, developed in Latvia, permits ducklings to be ringed at an early age with a full-size ring without the ring falling off?
14. Where was the first bird observatory to introduce ringing in the early years of the 20th century?
15. What does the EURING (the European Union for Bird Ringing) age code 5 signify?
16. To within a year either way, when was EURING established to standardise methodology and terminology?
17. What symbol is used for a sight record of an identifiable colour ring, or to indicate that the ring number of a ringed bird was read in the field?
18. What is the only species ringed in Britain which is recovered regularly in Egypt?
19. Up to the end of the 1980s only two foreign-ringed Great Shearwaters had been recovered in Britain and Ireland. Where were they ringed?
20. After France and Spain, from which non-European country have most British and Irish ringed Manx Shearwaters been recovered?
21. To where do almost all drake Goosanders from Western Europe migrate to moult?
22. What is the German term used to describe the restless state of birds immediately before they set out on migration?
23. What is Europe's most threatened migrant?
24. What is the world's best travelled migrant?
25. What morphological feature would prevent a Swallow from being satellite-tracked whilst on migration?
26. Two globally threatened trans-Saharan migrants regularly occur in the UK. Name them.

27. In 1984 Duncan Parish of IWRB was handed a ring by a hunter in Thailand (who had killed and eaten the bird two years earlier). On checking up he discovered that he had personally ringed the bird in 1981. What was the species?

Ornithological Literature

1. *Enjoying Ornithology* was published by Poyser in 1983 as a celebration of the BTO's first 50 years. But who wrote the earlier book of the same name, published in 1965?
2. Which two islands provide the setting for Richard Perry's *Watching Seabirds*?
3. Who were the four authors of the original *Handbook of British Birds*?
4. Who wrote the introduction to the first edition of *A Field Guide to the Birds of Britain and Europe* by Peterson, Mountfort and Hollom?
5. Who is the present editor of *Wildfowl*? [N.B. 1992]
6. Who was the artist for Dresser's (1884-86) *Monograph of the Meropidae*?
7. In which year was Niko Tinbergen's *The Herring Gull's World* published (to within one year)?
8. To whom did Gilbert White write his letters about Selborne?
9. What journal does the West African Ornithological Society produce?
10. Which bird had books written about it by both David Lack and Derek Bromhall?
11. Who wrote a series of books about expeditions which he led, including *Portrait of a Wilderness* and *Portrait of a River* about the Coto Donana and the Danube Delta respectively?
12. Which bird species was monographed by J. H. Gurney in 1913 and J. B. Nelson in 1978?
13. Whose *Life Histories of North American Birds*, published between 1919 and 1968, (some posthumously), are still among of the best sources of information about the birds of that continent?
14. Whose *Illustrated Manual of British Birds* published in 1889 and revised in 1899, was a standard until Witherby's *Practical Handbook of British Birds* appeared?
15. A Northumberland wood engraver illustrated a two-volume work on British birds spanning the end of the 18th and start of the 19th centuries. Who was he?

16. Which family of birds was monographed in 4 volumes by William Beebe in 1918, a work which has recently been reprinted?
17. Which British bird artist founded a bird observatory at Monk's House, Northumberland, and wrote and illustrated the book *The House on the Shore* about it?
18. With which important literary figure did Philip Lutley Sclater co-author *Argentine Ornithology*, published in two volumes in 1888-89?
19. Which family of birds has been monographed by Daniel Giraud Elliot, Richard Bowdler Sharpe, Tom Iredale, Thomas Gilliard, and William Cooper and Joseph Forshaw?
20. What is the journal of the American Ornithologists' Union called?
21. The famous American ornithologist William Beebe wrote a monograph on pheasants. Which other classic work did he write with the word 'pheasant' in the title?
22. Well-known ornithological publisher Christopher Helm has recently established a new company and commissioned an impressive array of new titles. Name the company.
23. The forthcoming *Handbook of Birds of the World* published in Spain by Lynx Edicions will be a major milestone in ornithological literature. Who is its chief editor?
24. Who is the author of the Croom Helm guide to *Seabirds*?
25. What is the world's most valuable bird book (in pecuniary terms)?

A 'DIVING' DUCK

GENERAL KNOWLEDGE 1992

1. Which bird features in the logo of the Leicestershire and Rutland Ornithological Society?
2. Which bird was caught in the slips during a 1930s Test Match between England and Australia?

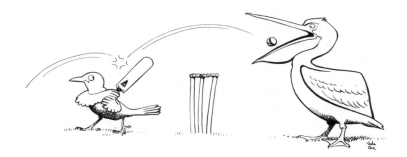

3. What is peculiar about the feeding method of the Galapagos Woodpecker Finch?
4. What was the most ubiquitous species in the first *Atlas of Breeding Birds in Britain and Ireland*, appearing in 90% of 10-km squares?
5. How many 10-km squares (whole and part) make up Britain and Ireland?
6. Where does the word 'tetrad' come from?
7. The Swift carries its greatest enemy with it. What is it?
8. BoEE is the abbreviation for what?
9. In which county did the first Cetti's Warbler occur in Britain, in October 1962?
10. The Wildfowl & Wetlands Trust's National Wildfowl Counts (renamed National Waterfowl Counts in 1991) began in which year?
11. Which way does the Kiwi face on a tin of shoe polish?
12. What gull might you be reminded of looking at an elephant?
13. What is the name of the RSPB's reserve on North Uist?
14. How many Ramsar sites are there in the UK?
15. What kind of bird is a Bearded Helmet-crest?
16. How many feathers (to the nearest 1,000) are there on a Bewick's Swan?
17. What is Britain's only endemic bird?
18. Why would you be surprised to see *Rhodonessa caryophyllacea*?
19. What is the new BOU official name for the Dunnock?

20. Which common British breeding bird moults completely twice each year?
21. Which of the following four species has undergone a population decline in Britain in recent years: Kestrel, Oystercatcher, Blackcap or Nuthatch?
22. Which family of birds is restricted to the Palaearctic realm?
23. Which species has been known to dive to a depth of 265 metres and for 15 minutes duration?
24. What is polygynandry?
25. What is the odd species out among the following: European Bee-eater, European Kingfisher, Long-tailed Tit and Dunnock, and why think breeding behaviour?
26. The Barn Owl will be put on Schedule 9 of the Wildlife and Countryside Act later this year (1992). What effect will this have?
27. The latest BTO survey of Peregrines puts the UK population at 1050 pairs at least. What was the population at its lowest level in 1964 (plus or minus 50)?
28. Which species of raptor has the greatest difference in relative size between male and female?
29. In which county is Hilbre Bird Observatory?
30. How would you tell a Tawny Owl pellet from a Barn Owl pellet?
31. Why do crows bury shellfish (mussels) in the ground, apart from as part of a food store?
32. Where in the world would you find the Silktail, Golden Dove and Shining Parrot?
33. Where in the world would you find the Bristlehead, Bulwer's Pheasant and Black Oriole?
34. Which bird observatory would you be visiting if you took a boat from Grutness?
35. Which well-known bird site would you be visiting if you took a boat from Seahouses?
36. Which member of the rail family has been recorded only once in Britain when it was caught on a fishing boat off Great Yarmouth on New Year's Day in 1902?
37. In which group of British birds can the young fly before they are fully grown?
38. Which passerine winters in internationally important numbers around the shores of The Wash?
39. Which exotic-looking vagrant to Britain has bred here on two occasions - near Edinburgh in 1920 and in Sussex in 1955?
40. The introduction of what device from Japan in 1956 revolutionised bird ringing?

41. The distribution of the plant Fumitory is closely related in Britain to the range of which bird, for which it is an important food plant?
42. Of which colonial nesting species is the largest British colony in the Grampian region?
43. Which aspect of bird study did the brothers Richard and Cherry Kearton pioneer in this country in the 1890s?
44. What species, an exceptional vagrant to Britain, actually nested successfully at Cambridge Sewage Farm in 1946?
45. In which tropical family does the male wall up the female in the nest hole for the duration of nesting?
46. What important discovery was made in 1861 in a quarry near Solnhofen, Bavaria?
47. Which small bird was formerly the object of a hunt on St Stephen's Day in many parts of England?
48. What bird is used as the symbol of the Irish Wildbird Conservancy?
49. What bird is used as the symbol of the Scottish Ornithologists' Club?
50. In legend, where did the Halcyon (or Kingfisher) build its nest?
51. Which ornithologically important wetland straddles the Austrian and Hungarian border?
52. Which British breeding seabirds feed mainly by 'klepto-parasitism'?
53. How many tail feathers do all European passerines (with one exception) have?
54. What bird is used as the symbol of the British Ornithologists' Union?
55. What is the world's fastest surface-swimming duck?
56. What is the only bird species known to hibernate?
57. Which bird species has the most subspecies?
58. Which seabird balances its egg on a bare branch?
59. Which bird species is thought to build the largest nest?
60. Which threatened Indonesian bird buries its eggs in the ground?
61. Which species has the longest migration?
62. Which is the fastest-running bird which can also fly?
63. Which trans-Saharan migrant mimics up to 40 other birds in its song?
64. Which bird has the longest bill in relation to its body size?
65. Which two taxonomists recently revolutionised ornithological thinking on the order of bird families?
66. How many globally threatened species breed in the UK?

BIRDFAIR 1993
Polish Wetlands Project

Poland is one of the richest countries in Europe for birds, as much of the natural forest, marsh and wetlands still exist. Five globally threatened species breed in Poland, including Corncrake and Aquatic Warbler. Significant populations of Little Bittern, Bittern and Great Snipe are attracted to the vast wetlands. Areas along the Baltic coast are host to thousands of grebes, diving ducks and geese throughout the winter. The BirdLife partner in Poland, OTOP, was formed in 1992 and Birdfair 1993 donated £40,000 to help protect some of these key sites. This sum, with help from Swarovski Optik, bought for OTOP the Karsiborska Kepa Reserve, which lies in the mouth of the River Swina in northwest Poland. This 300-hectare reserve holds up to 1% of the world's population of Aquatic Warblers and has excellent visitor facilities including paths, information boards and leaflets, and an observation tower. Bird monitoring is in place to ensure that water and grazing levels are maintained to create optimum breeding conditions for the reserve's wealth of birds. OTOP successfully campaigned to reduce the recreational development of the Swina Delta. A book covering the 118 IBAs in Poland has been published and distributed to decision makers and planners to create a greater awareness of the country's most valuable wildlife sites. OTOP is also working on a collaborative project to protect the Chelm Marshes.

The contestants, under the Chairmanship of Bill Oddie, were:-

Chris Mead (British Trust for Ornithology)
Colin Bibby (BirdLife International)
Myrfyn Owen (Wildfowl & Wetlands Trust)
* Ian Dawson (Royal Society for the Protection of Birds)

SPECIALIST SUBJECTS 1993
Migration

1. Black-throated Accentor is non-migratory and therefore an unlikely candidate for vagrancy to the UK. True or false?
2. Three migrant shorebirds winter in Australia in numbers above 200,000. Great Knot, Red-necked Stint and . . .?
3. Which of the following Conventions deals specifically with migrants, Bern or Bonn?
4. The Bonn Convention calls upon parties to make agreements between themselves to further the conservation of migratory species. To date, how many such agreements have been signed?
5. Which way do migrating Aquatic Warblers head when leaving their breeding grounds in Poland?
6. Who was the author of *The Migrations of Birds*, published in the UK in 1962 by Heinemann?
7. What is the name of the phenomenon where a resident bird pairs with a migrant of the same species in winter quarters and then migrates north with it?
8. Which word, associated with bird migration, usually appears last in the index of any book about the subject?
9. Approximately what percentage (to within 5%) of a Sedge Warbler's weight is fat when it commences its autumn migration?
10. What is the name of the pair of hills overlooking Istanbul and the Bosphorus, which are famous as a migration watchpoint?
11. Which is the smallest avian intercontinental migrant?
12. Where do most British male Goosanders go to moult?
13. How many refuelling stops does a Hudsonian Godwit make between Hudson Bay and Patagonia?
14. A Manx Shearwater was taken from a Welsh colony to Boston, Massachusetts. How many days did it take after release to find its nesting burrow?
15. Where would you be if you were studying visible migration in Lizarrieta?
16. Where do the majority of Europe's Eleanora's Falcons spend the winter?
17. Where do British wintering Knots breed?
18. Where does the Atitlan Grebe migrate to in winter?

19. Where do Spanish-breeding Shelducks moult?
20. Which two species have provided the majority of British and Irish ringing controls in Senegal?

The Dartford Warbler

1. What was the UK population low for Dartford Warbler after the winter of 1962/63?
2. Which has occurred further north in Britain, Dartford Warbler or Marmora's Warbler?
3. The scientific name of Dartford Warbler is *Sylvia undata*. What does *undata* mean?
4. What feature is best used to define racial differences amongst Dartford Warbler populations?
5. The Dartford Warbler shares its name with a famous tunnel. How much is the toll to drive through this tunnel (to within 10p)?

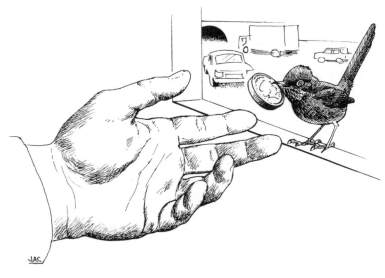

6. Which country is believed to hold the largest population of Dartford Warblers?
7. Which English county now holds the most Dartford Warblers?
8. Where in Hampshire has the Dartford Warbler been usurped by the Badger?
9. In how many African countries do Dartford Warblers breed regularly?

10. Are there more records of Dartford Warblers for Scotland or Ireland?
11. What is the main threat to the survival of Dartford Warbler as a British species?
12. The Dartford Warbler was first described in Britain from a specimen taken at which locality near Dartford?
13. In which year?
14. In which year (to within five) was the first record of a Dartford Warbler in Scotland?
15. Which of the following is not a local English name for the Dartford Warbler: Furze Wren, Red-eye, French Blackbird?
16. What is the most likely fruit which might be eaten by British Dartford Warblers in autumn?
17. What is the most frequent clutch size of Dartford Warblers in England?
18. Dartford Warbler is usually double-brooded, but where in its range is it always single-brooded?
19. On average, which is the longest primary in a Dartford Warbler?
20. According to BWP, which of the races *dartfordiensis*, *undata* and *toni* is the only one in which the length of the bill, measured to the base of the skull, is longer in the male than the female?

Geese of the World

1. If its scientific name was translated literally, which goose would be known as the Red-footed Goose?
2. According to *Wildfowl* by Madge and Burn, which is the most abundant race of Canada Goose after the race *interior*?
3. How often do grazing European White-fronted Geese *Anser a. albifrons* defaecate?
4. Which is the most southerly species of *Branta* goose?
5. By how much has the population of Siberian Bean Goose grown over the last 30 years?
6. How can juvenile Ross's Goose best be separated from juvenile Snow Goose?
7. If you saw a wild goose in Hawaii, you would be sure it was a Nene, or would you?
8. To what altitude do Bar-headed Geese commonly nest (to within 500m)?
9. Two Western Palaearctic geese are considered globally threatened. Which?

10. Which species of goose is often held to be the link between 'true' geese and sheldgeese?
11. Which is the smallest race of Canada Goose?
12. How do the feet of Hawaiian Geese differ from those of other geese?
13. Which species of sheldgoose has individuals which moult their flight feathers progressively and so have no flightless period?
14. Which adult goose of the genus *Anser* has a bill which is predominantly yellow?
15. Name two species of wild geese that appear in ancient Egyptian paintings.
16. Why is the specific name of Nene *sandvicensis*?
17. Which goose breeds in the wilds of New Zealand?
18. Which is the commonest goose in Britain in the winter?
19. Which goose on the British list perches freely in trees?
20. What have geese, swans and British Telecom got in common?

Starlings of the World

1. Sometimes known as 'tickbirds', these two African members of the starling family are best told apart by their bill colours. What are they normally called?
2. Which colonially nesting starling from Sulawesi bores its nest-holes in trees?
3. Although called the Military Starling, this bird does not belong to the starling family. Of which family is it a member?
4. Which genus of starlings is found throughout the Pacific?
5. What name, relating to plumage, is often given to the genus *Lamprotornis*?
6. Which starling has largely white plumage?
7. Pliny wrote of Rose-coloured Starlings "they are never seen except when their protection is needed". Why were they so valued?
8. How many starling species are native to Australia?
9. How many races of the Common Starling breed in Britain and Ireland, according to the BOU?
10. Which starling genus contains the most species?
11. Which species of starling has been used in medicine to investigate both cancer and baldness?
12. Which species of starling has only been recorded once in Britain before 1993?

13. Name either African species of starling listed as Near Threatened or Vulnerable.
14. What was the status of the Bali Starling in the wild in 1993?
15. Which starling might you expect to find combing the Giant Lobelias of Mount Kenya for snails?
16. How many starling species are considered to be globally threatened?
17. The Common Starling is resident in both Iceland and Lapland. True or false.
18. Any starling seen in Morocco can be ticked as a Spotless. True or false?

GENERAL KNOWLEDGE 1993

1. What colour is a Great Tit's forehead?
2. Who wrote *The Starling*, published by Oxford University Press?
3. What bird is the emblem of Guatemala?
4. Where would a birdwatcher find Eday, Sanday and Copinsay?
5. To which family does the Mistletoebird belong?
6. What is a Mudlark?
7. Which is the only wader that lays white eggs?
8. Where in Britain would a knowledgeable twitcher go for 'PG Tips'?

9. Which fish owl occurring in Japan, China and Siberia wades through the shallows in search of crayfish?
10. In much of Asia which Euro-urbanite is replaced by its arboreal cousin?
11. Which of the world's bird species is best equipped to kill people?
12. Which parrot commonly exhibits lekking behaviour?
13. What talent do Oilbirds and Cave Swiftlets share?
14. What is the liquid connection between Emperor Penguins, the Greater Flamingo and pigeons?
15. Which species derived its scientific name from two of its British breeding colonies?

16. Young birds start with Neossoptiles, and change them for Teleoptiles. What are they?
17. What colour is an adult Pochard's eye?
18. Who wrote *British Warblers*, published by Collins?
19. What bird is the state emblem of Western Australia?
20. Ben Jonson likened Shakespeare to which bird?
21. Where would a birdwatcher find Morston, Waxham and Weybourne?
22. Where can a catbird meet a mousebird?
23. What do Livingstone, Bannerman and Lady Ross all have named after them?
24. Name two species whose English names celebrate Russian rivers?
25. Parrots do not migrate. True or false?
26. If you find a 'Rosefinch' on the Scillies, showing a supercilium and extensively streaked underparts, which North American 'first' might you be looking at?
27. On which Caribbean island would you find a relict population of Two-barred Crossbill?
28. The Vulturine Parrot is carnivorous. True or false?
29. How many differences (to the nearest 10) are there between the current British Ornithologists' Union list of bird names , and that of names proposed by Sharrock and Inskipp on behalf of the BOU, published recently in *British Birds*?
30. How many of these proposed changes should the BOU adopt?
31. In which area are the most Budgerigars found: Australia or the rest of the world?
32. To what group of birds do Aracaris belong?
33. By what name is the Windhover more commonly known?
34. What colour is the throat of a Kingfisher?
35. Who wrote *Weather and Bird Behaviour*, published by Poyser?
36. Where would a birdwatcher find Annet, Samson and Gugh?
37. Where would you look for a crissum?
38. Which bird is named after the Greek goddess of wisdom?
39. Which is the only bird that has been recorded eating Deadly Nightshade berries in Britain?
40. Which gull on the British list has two complete moults each year?
41. Which bird is found only in Spain, Portugal and Eastern Asia?
42. A flufftail is a real bird. True or false?
43. What is the British record for the most bird species seen in 24 hours?
44. What name do the English use for the bird that the Americans call a 'Dovekie'?

45. Which group of birds do sailors refer to as 'Man o' War Birds'?
46. From when does *Archaeopteryx* date?
47. What is the other name for the Sprosser?
48. In which direction does the upper mandible of a Crossbill bend with respect to the lower mandible?
49. Which is the most species-rich continent for birds?
50. Which bird features on the front cover of *The Atlas of Wintering Birds in Britain and Ireland*, published by Poyser?
51. Who wrote *Wild Geese*, published by Poyser?
52. What is the State bird of Hawaii?
53. What colour are an adult Kittiwake's legs?
54. What is the most size-dimorphic passerine in Europe?
55. Which is the only sandpiper (member of Scolopacidae) that breeds regularly in Africa? (excluding the African Snipe and Madagascar Snipe).
56. Which is the odd one out: Chukar, Bobwhite, Phainopepla or Kiskadee?
57. Which is the only nocturnal fruit-eating bird?
58. What is *Melopsittacus undulatus* more commonly known as?
59. The white and grey cranes of Asia are the Siberian and Sarus. What are their North American equivalents?
60. How is the American race of Whimbrel most readily separated from the Eurasian?
61. In the USA, the Great Northern Diver is known as the Common Loon. What is the Black-throated Diver known as?
62. Arctic Warbler breeds in the USA. True or false?
63. The 'Basel sequence' is currently being questioned by Sibley and Monroe. What is it?
64. What type of bird is a Peruvian Sheartail?
65. In which year was the last confirmed sighting of the Dodo? (within 10 years)?
66. How many full species of bird are known to have become extinct between 1600 and 1985?

BIRDFAIR 1994
Project Halmahera

Halmahera is an 18,000km² island, about 3,000km north east of Java, with a bird list of more than 213 bird species, of which 206 are resident. Halmahera, together with the smaller associated islands of Bacan and Morotai, is home to an incredible 26 species of birds that are found nowhere else in the world. Birdfair raised £41,000 in 1994 for Project Halmahera. These funds were used by BirdLife Indonesia to evaluate the biological diversity and conservation requirements of two areas on Halmahera: Lalo Bata (1,400 km²) and Ake Tajawe (7,400 km²). The surveys found 21 endemic species in Ake Tajawe and 23 in Lalo Bata. Other discoveries included the largest known nesting ground for the Moluccan Scrubfowl and the first recorded nest of Wallace's Standardwing, as well as an important display area used by up to 40 male standardwings; this site later featured in the BBC programme Attenborough in Paradise. Sadly, in 1998/99, just as a proposal for the establishment of protected area boundaries was produced, trouble flared up in the Maluku region, putting a stop to all further action. In January 2004, BirdLife was able to re-establish connections in Halmahera and received a very favourable response from the provincial government to reinstate the original programme. In April 2004, a rapid assessment team returned to Maluku to reassess the biodiversity, forest cover, social economy, local government policy and the political situation. Already, 36 IBA sites have been identified for the Maluku region and an IBA directory will be published in 2004.

The contestants, under the Chairmanship of Bill Oddie, were:-

Paul Green (British Trust for Ornithology)
* Bob Scott (Royal Society for the Protection of Birds)
Barry Hughes (Wildfowl & Wetlands Trust)
Paul Jepson (BirdLife International)

SPECIALIST SUBJECTS 1994
Crows of the Genus Corvus

1. What species is endemic to Halmahera, Morotai and Obi?
2. What is the palest race of the House Crow *Corvus splendens*?
3. Which is the most widespread *Corvus* species in Africa?
4. To what area of Hawaii is the Hawaiian Crow or Alala now confined?
5. What is the scientific name of the Torresian Crow?

6. In 1967 a new species of crow was 'discovered'. Where?
7. When do Rooks get their bare faces?
8. How much does a Common Raven weigh?
9. Apart from Antarctica, which continent does not have *Corvus* crows?
10. Rooks are often at risk in hot dry summer weather. Why?
11. Which *Corvus* species is the only crow found in New Zealand, although it was introduced?
12. What facial feature do adult Long-billed Crow, Australian (Torresian) Crow, Little Crow, Australian Raven, Little Raven and Forest Raven have in common?

13. Name one of the islands where the Palm Crow *Corvus palmarum* can be found.
14. How does the Northwestern Crow manage to eat mussels?
15. What did Edgar Allan Poe's Raven say?
16. How many accepted European records have there been of Daurian Jackdaw?
17. What is the age at which a ringed Carrion Crow which is retrapped must be reported to the BTO?
18. How many races of Raven are recognised in a) Europe, and b) Asia and North America?
19. Three of the four common *Corvus* species in the UK have identical numbers of flight feathers. Which one differs and how?
20. Name two of the four *Corvus* species listed in the ICBP Checklist of Threatened Birds (first edition). [For a bonus, how many species are now considered threatened?]

RSPB Reserves

1. What are the names of the three 'Valley Lakes' (now 'Valley Wetlands') at the RSPB reserve of the same name on Anglesey?
2. On which RSPB reserve was the UK's first Red-necked Stint recorded?
3. To within 5%, what percentage of the species of macro-moths resident in the UK do RSPB reserves support?
4. How many Red Data Species of plant occur on RSPB reserves?
5. Where did Jeremy Sorenson start his career with the RSPB?
6. Near which reserve are the Midrips?
7. What is the most common nestbox species at the Gwenfrwdd?
8. At Snettisham roosting flocks of which species sometimes top 100,000 birds?
9. What London borough is associated with Arne?
10. Why was Cheyne Court, purchased by the RSPB in 1930, disposed of a few years later?
11. How much land does the RSPB own in Orkney?
12. For what species was Balranald particularly established?
13. What is the main habitat type at Nagshead in Gloucestershire?
14. Which is the oldest extant RSPB reserve?
15. When was it established – to within 5 years?
16. Which RSPB reserve surrounds Scott's Hall?
17. Millom railway station is the nearest to which RSPB reserve?
18. The Weaver's Way Footpath passes through which RSPB reserve?

19. How much did the RSPB pay Peter de Savery for the Hayle Estuary reserve?
20. When did the first young Gannet fledge from Bempton Cliffs - 1938, 1943 or 1948?

The Ruddy Duck

1. What is the German name for the Ruddy Duck?
2. In what country was the type specimen for the species taken?
3. The nominate race is *jamaicensis*. Name one of the other two races.
4. Which is the largest of the subspecies of Ruddy Duck?
5. According to Bellrose *et al.* in which direction is the sex ratio most often skewed in adult Ruddy Duck populations?
6. What is the seasonal change in coloration of the bill of male Ruddy Ducks?
7. In North America the Ruddy Duck is also commonly known as the "Bull-necked........" Complete the name.
8. In which genus was the Ruddy Duck originally placed?
9. Which is the most southerly country in which the North American Ruddy Duck (i.e. *Oxyura j jamaicensis*) has been recorded?
10. Which mainland European country hosted the first breeding record of the North American Ruddy Duck?
11. Who collected the type specimen of Ruddy Duck?
12. Which of the following names is not a nickname for the Ruddy Duck: 'blatherskite', 'hickory-head', or 'bubblebreast'?
13. Ruddy Duck eggs are larger than Mallard eggs. True or false?
14. How many Ruddy Ducks arrived at Slimbridge from North America in 1948 and 1949?
15. What colour are the webs of the feet of an adult male Ruddy Duck?
16. How much does a drake weigh?
17. At what age is the duckling fully feathered?
18. Where would a Ruddy Duck drake with no white on the cheeks come from?
19. What is the average clutch size in the wild?
20. What happened to the wild population some 100 years ago?

Birds of Indonesia

1. If you had a really good day's birding, and saw an owlet-nightjar, a bulbul, a friarbird and two birds of paradise, where is the only place in the world you could be?
2. Which woodcock occurs only on two islands in Indonesia and on New Guinea?
3. Name three species of stork that are resident in the Greater Sundas.
4. Where is the only place the Dusky Munia occurs?
5. How many endemic kingfishers does Halmahera have?
6. Why would *Habroptila wallacii* be difficult to see?
7. Which Indonesian bird is known only from a female collected at the foot of Kelabat Volcano, Sulawesi in 1931, by Heinrich?
8. Which bird has the Indonesian name Wowo-wiwi?
9. What is the title of the Bulletin of the Indonesian Ornithological Society?
10. How many species of barbets can be found in Wallacea?
11. What is the name of the rare migrant wader *Numenius madagascarensis* that passes through on its way to winter in Australia?
12. What is the English name of the genus of forest birds, half a dozen of which occur in the region, nearly all with brilliant red on them?
13. Which is the bigger of the two pelicans found in Indonesia?
14. How much does a Scarlet Sunbird weigh, to the nearest gram?
15. What are the two main colours of the male *Irena puella*?
16. Which Indonesian endemic has not been seen since 1987, and is believed to be extinct?
17. Which Indonesian bird's call has been described as "the sound of eyes being plucked from their sockets"? (if you are familiar with that sound!)?
18. Which bird is endemic to the island of Boano in the South Moluccas: a) White-tipped Monarch, b) Slaty Monarch or c) Black-chinned Monarch?
19. Which bird is known only from two specimens collected from Sumatra in 1917 and doubtfully from Peninsular Malaysia?
20. Name the two species of *Zoothera* thrushes endemic to the Tanimbar Islands.

GENERAL KNOWLEDGE 1994

1. Which species of bird is collectively known in flight as a wisp?
2. Which is the odd one out: Sleepy Cisticola, Lazy Cisticola or Foxy Cisticola?
3. What colour legs does a Black Guillemot have?
4. To which continent would you go to see a Chachalaca?
5. What kind of bird is a Surfbird?
6. How many toes does a Three-toed Woodpecker have?
7, What often-used British bird's name has an 'x' in it?
8. Where is Cristin?
9. Which is the odd one out: Black Bishop, White Bishop or Red Bishop?
10. What is the national bird of South Africa: Crowned Crane, Blue Crane or Wattled Crane?
11. What is the more usual name for the Rain Goose?
12. According to *Birds in Wales*, which of the following has been recorded breeding in Wales since 1900: Little Shearwater, Leach's Petrel or Wryneck.
13. Who wrote the *Dictionary of Birds* almost 100 years ago?
14. How old was Max Nicholson at his last birthday? (i.e. in July 1994)
15. What species of bird, in the wild, has the biggest biomass in Britain?
16. Which species of bird is collectively known as an exultation?
17. Which is the odd one out: Laughing Cisticola, Rattling Cisticola or Tinkling Cisticola?
18. What colour bill does an adult Kittiwake have?
19. To which continent would you go to see a Turaco?
20. What kind of bird is a Kaka?
21. What is the name of the foot structure in which two toes point forward and two toes point backward?
22. Where would you meet a Coquette (ornithologically)?
23. In Northumberland, which famous artist almost ran an Observatory at Monks House?
24. Which of the following is most rarely recorded in the UK: *Glareola maldivarum*, *Glareola pratincola* or *Glareola nordmanni*?
25. Which of the following has a bird observatory: Skokholm, Skomer or Grassholm?
26. Which of the following is the only one to have been recorded more than once in Wales: King Eider, Arctic Warbler or Blackpoll Warbler?

27. According to Sibley and Monroe, to which group of birds does the Kagu belong: Cranes, Nightjars or Pigeons?
28. What bird is used as the symbol of the Oriental Bird Club?
29. Which species in Europe is the sole member of a widespread family in America?
30. The *New Atlas* has Wren as the most common breeding bird in Britain and Ireland. Within a million, how many territories?
31. What do South American seabirds and Broadway have in common?
32. Which film star has a daughter who majored in ornithology?
33. Which species of bird is collectively known as a murmuration?
34. Which is the odd one out: Black-backed Cisticola, Black-necked Cisticola or Black-winged Cisticola?
35. What colour legs does an Alpine Chough have?
36. To which continent would you go to see a fairy-wren?
37. What kind of bird is a Dollarbird?
38. Out of Africa, Asia and the Americas, which has no bulbuls?
39. What went extinct 150 years ago this June? (1994 quiz, remember).
40. Which artist is associated particularly with Gannets and the Bass Rock?
41. Which of the following is recorded most rarely in the UK: *Phylloscopus fuscatus, Phylloscopus schwarzi* or *Phylloscopus armandii*?
42. What colour is the bill of a Goldfinch?
43. After which bird is the Suffolk Ornithologists' Club's newsletter named?
44. After which bird is the Wiltshire Ornithological Society's annual report named?
45. What birds did W. B. Yeats count at Coole Park and how many of them were there?
46. On which island would you find Campbell Island Teal?
47. Who edited the *New Dictionary of Birds*?
48. Who first realised that there were three *Phylloscopus* warblers breeding in Britain?
49. What is OTOP?
50. Which species of bird is collectively known as a charm?
51. Which is the odd one out: Rock-loving Cisticola, Tree-perching Cisticola or Cloud-scraping Cisticola?
52. What colour bill does a Magpie have?
53. To which continent would you go to see a leafbird?
54. What type of bird is a Snowcap?

55. What single name British bird has five 'e's in it?
56. Which is the odd one out: Bananaquit, Orangequit or Raspberryquit?
57. What pheasant is the national bird of Nepal: Impeyan Pheasant, Satyr Tragopan or Blood Pheasant?
58. In Wales which warbler was recorded in the fewest squares during the latest breeding bird atlas?
59. Which of the following American warblers has not been recorded in Wales: Yellow-rumped Warbler, Black and White Warbler or Yellow Warbler?
60. Which two resident British species were only separated 100 years ago?
61. Which two small birds may lay blue eggs in a nest-box?
62. From which country do Roseate Terns from Britain mostly get recovered in winter?
63. Whose paradox is concerned with migration between the Palaearctic and Africa?
64. In which country is *Le Gerfaut* published?
65. Who edited the latest *Dictionary of Birds* (1985)?
66. Where does/did 'Grandma' live?

BIRDFAIR 1995
Moroccan Wetlands Project

Morocco's 3,000km coastline contains many internationally important wetlands used as staging posts by both migratory and wintering birds. In a country where much of the land is barren desert, water is a precious natural resource. 60% of the population of Morocco is concentrated along the coast, bringing great pressures on the natural wetlands. Already, 70% of Morocco's coastal wetlands have disappeared. The 1995 Birdfair raised £45,000, which was devoted to two different sites. The first, Sidi Bou-Rhaba Nature Reserve, one of five Ramsar sites in the country, holds the largest known breeding population of the globally threatened Marbled Teal. The reserve lies in the northern region of Morocco, near the city of Kenitra, and Birdfair funds helped build the National Environmental Education Centre based at the reserve. The centre is now fully operational and receives many visitors from both schools and the general public. The second site, Merja Zerga, is best known as being one of the sites where the critically endangered Slender-billed Curlew used to occur. Merja Zerga is by far the most important wetland in Morocco. In 1997, BirdLife International signed an agreement with the Moroccan government to work together to continue to develop project activities for wetlands and other threatened habitats. BirdLife's partner in Spain, SEO, is responsible for the BirdLife Morocco Country Programme and, with the information gathered by Birdfair funding, has secured, in 2004, significant funding to implement a project on actions for the sustainable long-term use of the natural resources at Merja Zerga.

The contestants, under the Chairmanship of Chris Packham, were:-

Mike Crewe (British Trust for Ornithology)
Peter Cranswick (Wildfowl & Wetlands Trust)
Gary Allport (BirdLife International)
* Tim Melling (Royal Society for the Protection of Birds)

SPECIALIST SUBJECTS 1995
Sylvia Warblers

1. How many races of Whitethroat are recognised by Cramp *et al.* (1992) in *Birds of the Western Palaearctic*?
2. Which species of *Sylvia* warbler has, on average, the shortest wing?
3. What are the two main features separating *Sylvia sarda sarda* and *S. sarda balearica*?
4. Where would you find the rare melanistic form of the *heineken* race of Blackcap?

5. Is the white crescent in the eye of an adult Lesser Whitethroat above or below the pupil?
6. Which European country has the second highest breeding population of Orphean Warbler?
7. What is the current population trend of Cyprus Warbler?
8. What is the main feature which would enable you to distinguish a Spectacled Warbler from a Subalpine Warbler?
9. Which has the longer tail – a Sardinian Warbler or a Ménétries's Warbler?
10. Give the scientific name of the Cyprus Warbler.
11. Which of the warblers of the genus *Sylvia* has the most darkly coloured female?
12. What species of *Sylvia* warbler has a subspecies named after Hume?

13. With which other *Sylvia* warbler would you be most likely to confuse Marmora's Warbler, judging on appearance only?
14. Which species of *Sylvia* warbler have accents on their English names?
15. What English town is commemorated in the name of a *Sylvia* warbler?
16. Where are most foreign recoveries of Lesser Whitethroats in autumn?
17. Within one millimetre, what is the average difference between male and female Blackcap wings?
18. Who is *Sylvia mystacea* named after?
19. What is *Sylvia sarda*?
20. What is a Greater Pettychaps?
21. How many species of *Sylvia* warbler breed in Britain?
22. How many subspecies of Orphean Warbler breed in Europe?

Threatened Wildfowl

1. Which is the only county regularly to hold a population of Bean Geese?
2. Where was the Greenland race of the White-fronted Goose first recognised in the UK by Peter Scott?
3. Which species of wildfowl has more than 30% of its world population breeding in England?
4. Which Critically Endangered species of wildfowl may breed in the mountains on the border between China and North Korea?
5. Which Indian species of wildfowl, considered probably to be extinct, has been reported by hunters in Myanmar?
6. What has caused the Brazilian Merganser to become Critically Endangered?
7. Which species of goose had a world population in the wild of only 30-50 individuals before conservation action improved the situation?
8. What is the main wintering area for the Swan Goose?
9. Name two of the UK Dependent Territories on which the West Indian Whistling-Duck occurs?
10. What is the maximum number of White-headed Ducks now thought to winter in the Caspian Sea?
11. On what does the Laysan Duck primarily feed?
12. What is the current world population estimate for the Red-breasted Goose?

13. On which two islands does the Hawaiian Goose or Nene now occur?
14. What is/was the most important site for the Madagascar Pochard?
15. When was the last Crested Shelduck reliably seen?
16. Which very rare South American species is still numerous in the Falkland Islands?
17. Where does *Tachyeres leucocephalus* migrate to in winter?
18. The genus *Cairina* has only two species. One is the Muscovy Duck. What is the other?
19. On which two islands does Meller's Duck occur?
20. How much less than a drake Ruddy Duck does a drake White-headed Duck weigh?
21. Apart from Brazilian Merganser, what is the other very rare *Mergus* species?

Birds of Morocco

1. What is the upper limit of the estimated world population of Slender-billed Curlew?
2. Which introduced species of North American bird now occurs all year round in Morocco?
3. How many species of Sandgrouse occur in Morocco?
4. The first Western Palaearctic record of which North American species came from Morocco in January 1995?
5. While birding in Morocco in 1994, what did Bill Oddie term the local children who often accompanied him on his birding trips?
6. What is the name of the Moroccan BirdLife partner?
7. Is the Marbled Teal protected from hunting in Morocco?
8. Where in Morocco would you be most likely to find Slender-billed Curlews?
9. Which is the only one of nine North African breeding corvids to be confined to Morocco?
10. From which three countries do Morocco's wintering Greater Flamingos originate?
11. Which well-known British ornithologists published a paper *An ornithological journey in Morocco* in 1951?
12. Which seabird, with its world breeding population confined to the Mediterranean, has a significant wintering population on the Atlantic coast of Morocco?
13. What rings are normally used in Morocco?

14. Which British thrush regularly winters in important numbers in Morocco?
15. Who, from the BTO, went to Figuig over 30 years ago?
16. Within 200 how many British ringing recoveries had been reported from Morocco by the end of 1991?
17. How many species from British ringing have been found in Morocco (by 1995)?
18. Which rare Scottish breeding wader winters in Morocco?
19. Apart from Curlews, what else might you see that is Slender-billed?
20. How many species of swift breed in Morocco?
21. Apart from Great Spotted, what is the other breeding woodpecker in Morocco?
22. What is Morocco's smallest breeding bird?

British Warblers

1. What is the scientific name of the two northern races of Chiffchaff that occur in Britain on migration?
2. Of the warblers struck off the British list as a result of the 'Hastings Rarities Affair', which was the last to be reinstated)in 1977)?
3. Who is the author of the New Naturalist book *British Warblers*?
4. Where did a Bonelli's Warbler die to gain entry to the British list?
5. Which globally threatened warbler occurs annually on migration in Britain?
6. Between which two breeding seasons did the Whitethroat suffer a 77% decline in the British population?
7. Which British breeding warbler is most likely to have ringing recoveries from Lebanon, Israel or Egypt?
8. How many species of *Sylvia* have occurred in the UK?
9. What was the estimated breeding population of Wood Warblers, in terms of the number of singing males, in Britain (in 1993)?
10. In what year is Cetti's Warbler first thought to have bred in Britain?
11. How many accepted records of Blyth's Reed Warbler were there in the UK in the calendar year 1993?
12. The juveniles of which species of warbler can be separated from adults by their gorget of brown spots?
13. Which is the most abundant species of warbler breeding in Britain?

14. How many times is the letter 'e' found in the Latin name for the Sedge Warbler?
15. How many species of the genus *Regulus* regularly breed in the UK?
16. How many subspecies of the Chiffchaff are generally recognised?
17. What does the word *Phylloscopus* mean?
18. What is the Chiffchaff's closest relative in Britain?
19. What change occurs in the Blackcap's diet during the summer?
20. Which British warbler has been known in the past as "Black-headed hay-jack"?
21. Within 10%, how many species of birds is the Marsh Warbler known to mimic?

GENERAL KNOWLEDGE 1995

1. What is an arse-foot?
2. Which bird helped the wolf to feed Romulus and Remus?
3. Who wrote the New Naturalist monograph on the Wren?
4. According to Marlowe, who 'tolls the sick man's passport in her beak'?
5. Who edited *The Handbook of British Birds*?
6. Which European country has the largest wintering population of Common Cranes?
7. What is the name of the Shag in Noggin the Nog?
8. What would you hear reeling?
9. Which has the larger breeding population in the UK - Siskin or Goldfinch?
10. Which European country has the largest breeding population of Leach's Storm-Petrel?
11. Where is the largest breeding Bearded Tit colony in England?
12. What are Isle of Wight Parsons?
13. What is *Xenus cinereus*?
14. In the western Palaearctic which member of the Phasianidae breeds only in Morocco?

15. Where was Britain's first White-throated Robin seen?
16. Which European country has the largest breeding population of Greater Spotted Eagle?
17. What is a 'shite scouter'?
18. What bird was sacred to Pallas Athene?
19. Who wrote the New Naturalist monograph on the Redstart?
20. Which European country has the largest wintering population of Steller's Eider?
21. According to Meiklejohn why is the Shag a most peculiar bird?
22. What would you hear booming?
23. Which has the larger breeding population in the UK - Willow Tit or Marsh Tit?
24. Which European country has the largest breeding population of (European) Storm-Petrel?
25. Before it recolonised the UK in the 1940s, where was the Avocet's last regular breeding site?
26. What are 'butter bumps'?
27. What is Long-tailed Duck known as in the USA?
28. What is *Limicola falcinellus*?
29. Which member of the Rallidae has the bulk of its Western Palaearctic breeding population in Morocco?
30. Which European country has the largest breeding population of Golden Eagle?
31. Which saint restored a Robin to life?
32. What is the logo of the West Midlands Bird Club?
33. What is a 'bum-towel'?
34. In mythology what was Alcyone turned into?
35. Who wrote the New Naturalist monograph on the Wood Pigeon?
36. Who wrote *The Parlement of Foules*?
37. Which European country has the largest wintering population of Red-breasted Goose?
38. What would you hear 'sharming'?
39. What kind of bird is a Gon-gon?
40. Which has the larger breeding population in the UK – Robin or Dunnock?
41. Which European country has the largest breeding population of Pygmy Cormorants?
42. When did Cetti's Warbler first breed in Britain – 1962, 1967 or 1972?
43. Where did Mediterranean Gull first breed in Britain?
44. What is Black-necked Grebe known as in the USA?
45. What is *Micropalama himantopus*?
46. Where was Britain's first Ancient Murrelet seen?

47. Which European country has the largest breeding population of White-tailed Eagles?
48. After which bird is the Hampshire Ornithological Society's annual report named?
49. In Norfolk what is a 'willy'?
50. In mythology what was Philomel turned into?
51. Who wrote the New Naturalist monograph on the Hawfinch?
52. Who wrote the poem *Sedge Warblers*?
53. What did Kleinschmidt and Hartert 'discover' in 1897?
54. Which European country has the largest wintering population of Barnacle Goose?
55. When the wind was southerly what did Hamlet know a hawk from?
56. What would you hear drumming?
57. What has the larger breeding population in the UK - Yellow Wagtail or Grey Wagtail?
58. Which European country has the largest breeding population of Night Herons?
59. When did Scarlet Rosefinch first breed in Britain – 1977, 1982 or 1987?
60. What are Corpse Hounds?
61. What is White-billed Diver known as in the USA?
62. What is *Tryngites subruficollis*?
63. Which gulls breed in Morocco?
64. Where was Britain's first Aleutian Tern seen?
65. Which European country has the largest breeding population of Lesser Spotted Eagle?
66. What is the Ornithological Society of the Middle East's journal called?

BIRDFAIR 1996
Ke Go Forest Project

Vietnam has the largest and fastest growing human population and the lowest level of forest cover of any country in eastern Asia. Lowland forests have suffered to a disproportionate degree as they invariably occupy the land most sought-after for agriculture. Funds from the 1996 Birdfair were used to save the Ke Go Forest, which is now the largest remaining block of lowland forest in central Vietnam. More than 270 species of birds have been recorded and include the critically endangered Vietnamese Pheasant, which is found exclusively within the forest. BirdLife began its work in Ke Go in 1989 but it was the £50,000 raised by Birdfair that allowed the BirdLife International Vietnam Programme to implement the Ke Go Forest Project between 1997 and early 1999. The enthusiasm shown by the government of Vietnam following ministerial visits to the fair in 1996 was demonstrated in December 1996 when Ke Go was decreed a nature reserve. A total area of 24,801 hectares was identified, comprising a strict protection area of 2,537 hectares and a forest rehabilitation area of 4,264 hectares. A management board was formed in June 1997. The BirdLife Ke Go Forest Project has been invaluable for the Ke Go Nature Reserve. The management board currently has 68 permanent members of staff and 30 contracted staff based at the headquarters and the 5 guard stations. Two of the guard stations were funded by Birdfair, along with a provision of motorbikes and other field equipment. Training was funded for nature reserve staff and environmental education for teachers. The project gathered pace with several new conservation projects in the Ke Go area.

The contestants, under the Chairmanship of Bill Oddie, were:

John Callion (British Trust for Ornithology)
* John Bowler (Wildfowl & Wetlands Trust)
Andrew Grieve (Royal Society for the Protection of Birds)
Richard Grimmett (BirdLife International)

SPECIALIST SUBJECTS 1996
The New Atlas of Breeding Birds of Britain and Ireland

1. Who wrote the species account for the Nuthatch?
2. How many Moorhen territories were estimated in Britain in 1988-91?
3. What is the definition of a large open dot on the Change Maps in the Atlas?
4. Which English county has the most large open dots on the Change Map for Oystercatcher?
5. How many large filled dots are there in southern Ireland on the distribution map for Pied Flycatcher?
6. Which county, according to the Atlas, has the largest colony of Bearded Tits?
7. How does the location of this colony differ from most other breeding sites?
8. Which species had the highest British population estimate using the CBC method?
9. What was the British population estimate of this species (to the nearest million)?
10. Which species had the third highest population estimate in Ireland?
11. Which species was recorded in the most squares in Britain and Ireland?
12. From where did the author of the foreword write?
13. Of the species depicted in the logos of the organising societies, which occurred in the most squares?
14. What does 'edge puss' mean to an Atlas buff?
15. How many species of natural origin bred during the Atlas period?
16. The compilers declare seven names on the cover. Which of these has the most obvious connection with field studies of birds?
17. Which is the most widespread species which was not recorded in Ireland?
18. How many of the species authors have a tattoo on their left buttock?
19. Which species, that occurred in more than 15 squares, showed the greatest percentage increase in occupied squares between the two Atlases?
20. How can colour-blind readers interpret the abundance maps?

21. The map of which species of bird appears on the front of the dust jacket of the New Atlas?
22. What species of bird appears on the title page of the New Atlas?
23. Who was Chairman of the New Atlas Working Group?
24. Name one of the six species for which it was necessary to move or omit records from the Abundance Maps to maintain confidentiality.
25. Which species showed the greatest range contraction in Britain between the two Atlases?
26. According to the New Atlas, what proportion of the EC's population of Golden Plover breeds in Britain and Ireland? [1996 EC, remember.]
27. Who wrote the account for Green Woodpecker?
28. What is the total number of dots on all the distribution maps?
29. From how many 10-km squares were records received for the New Atlas?
30. Who drew the Red-necked Grebe vignette?

Swans of the World

1. There are seven bones in a giraffe's neck. How many in a swan's neck?
2. Who wrote in his *History of British Birds* "The swan is, perhaps, of all the others, the most beautiful living ornament of our lakes and rivers"?
3. Mute Swans in which the cygnets and juveniles are white are known as 'Polish Swans'. Why is it thought that this name was used?
4. What is the incubation period for Mute Swans?
5. In Greek mythology, who is said to have taken the form of a swan for the seduction of Leda?
6. What is the normal body temperature of a swan?
7. Swans in Britain were originally bred for food. Where is the last remaining swannery?
8. Which two London livery companies have rights, along with the Queen, to mark swans on the River Thames still?
9. What is the meaning of the term 'half-swan' in swan marking?
10. Someone once counted the number of feathers on a Whistling Swan. How many were there?
11. What was the name of the first swan that Sir Peter Scott named when he realised that individual Bewick's Swans could be identified by the pattern of yellow on their bills?

12. How does the Coscoroba Swan differ from other swans in the rearing of its young?
13. Which swan became extinct around the late 1500s?
14. What is the maximum weight recorded for the Mute Swan?
15. In what year did Tchaikovsky write the ballet Swan Lake?
16. Which of the European swans migrates furthest south?
17. Which of the two swans found in South America prefers the coastal regions?
18. Which swan lays the smallest egg?
19. In various Nordic/Celtic legends what were the swan-maidens famous for?
20. What is the difference between the profile of the bill of a Trumpeter Swan compared with a Whistling Swan?
21. What is the daily weight intake in kilograms of wet vegetable food by Mute Swans?
22. What is the average weight in kilograms of an adult male Bewick's Swan in the winter in England?
23. Which swan has been recorded as a vagrant in the Azores?
24. Other than Alaska, which area supported the last remaining Trumpeter Swans in the 1930s, from where the species was successfully translocated to rebuild its numbers?
25. Apart from the red basal knob, what colour is the bill of the adult Black-necked Swan?
26. What is strange about the breast feathers of the Coscoroba Swan?
27. Which poet wrote in the early part of the 17th Century about the

Whooper Swan: *Here in my vaster pools, as white as snow or milk In water black as Styx, swims the wild swan, the ilk.*

28. Who composed the *Lemminkainen Suite* and described the music as showing the swan of Tuonela mysteriously flying with the deep rhythm of buzzing Mute Swan primaries?

29. Who first identified Bewick's Swan as a separate species from Whooper Swan in his book published in 1824?

Identification of Palaearctic Waders

1. In which species, during its moult to winter plumage, is the breast "invaded with pale mottling, becoming pale grey-brown although retaining a dull white bar across the chest"?

2. Which species' commonest call is a piping 'Peet' usually extended into 'Pleet-weet-weet', which is sharper than that of Spotted Sandpiper?

3. Which of the two Western Palaearctic dowitchers has more numerous and thicker 'tiger-stripes' on its flanks in summer plumage?

4. How does the underwing of Slender-billed Curlew differ from that of the Curlew?

5. How do the typical calls of Greater and Lesser Yellowlegs differ?

6. Which pratincole has the longest middle claw?

7. Which species combines *Numenius*-like plumage with *Pluvialis*-like behaviour and glides on bowed wings like *Actitis* sandpipers on its breeding grounds?

8. Does the black bar on an Avocet's tail extend to the two outer tail feathers?

9. You are in southern Ireland and have caught a medium-sized snipe with 16 tail feathers. Which species is it?

10. Which is the shortest-billed race of Dunlin?

11. On the island of Amami-Oshima what is the wader with the shortish, rather stout yellowish legs, medium-length bill, barred flanks and long plain wings and tail?

12. In China, which small wader has a complete black breastband, a black bill with a touch of colour at the base of the lower mandible, a barely discernible wingbar and a descending call?

13. Which wader has jet-black axillaries in all plumages, no contrast between rump and tail and is a very rare vagrant to the UK?

14. Which wader is most likely to be found underground?

15. A party of waders, all the same species, includes some birds with

red legs, some orange, some yellow and some greenish. What species is it?

16. Which two Palaearctic plovers have chestnut and black patches on the belly in breeding plumage?

17. Which wader has a bill clearly longer than its bright yellow-ochre tarsi?

18. You find a wader's skull and measure its bill at just over 8 inches. What is it and which sex?

19. Which two vagrant waders to the Western Palaearctic have a double black breastband?

20. What colour legs does a Purple Sandpiper have?

21. What wader has an orange rump?

22. What is the main distinguishing feature that separates Stone Curlew from Senegal Thick-knee?

23. Name the most obvious structural difference between Nordmann's Greenshank and Common Greenshank other than bill shape?

24. Red-breasted Snipe is a Nearctic vagrant. By what name is it now known?

25. In winter plumage, name the facial feature that can sometimes be used to separate Little from Red-necked Stint?

26. Which species has extensive unmarked orange underparts in adult plumage and breeds in the Palaearctic?

27. Name the most diagnostic feature that can be used to separate all plumages of Greater and Lesser Sand Plovers in flight?

28. What is Bonaparte's Sandpiper now more aptly known as?

29. Other than Oystercatcher, which vagrant Palaearctic species has a red eye-ring?

Birds of Egypt

1. Which species, formerly more widespread in the Western Palaearctic, now breeds only in the Gebel Elba area?

2. Which species of sparrow is also confined to this part of Egypt?

3. Which sparrow possibly breeds only in the extreme south-west of Egypt?

4. Which species, depicted on the walls of Pharaoh's tombs, no longer occurs in Egypt?

5. Which Egyptian god is usually depicted with the head of an ibis?

6. Which species, not previously known to breed in Egypt, has recently been recorded near Cairo where it is suspected of breeding?

7. How many species of wheatear regularly breed in Egypt?
8. In what year did the Ramsar Convention come into force in Egypt?
9. How many wetlands are currently designated under the Ramsar Convention in Egypt? (In 1996).
10. Which formerly bird-rich wetland, one of only four in Egypt listed in the Project Aquila inventory of 1971, has now almost disappeared?
11. A new species for Egypt was recently (1992) described on the basis of 2000-year-old evidence. What was it?
12. *Balearica pavonina* is not admitted to the Egyptian list although there are four claims. What is its English name?
13. Egypt has added a number of Afrotropical species to the Western Palaearctic list. What and when was the most recent (in 1996)?
14. Which common British bird has nested in the Nile Delta and other parts of northern Egypt since 1984?
15. Which lark was discovered to breed in Sinai in 1990?
16. Where did Michael Nicoll, founding father of Egyptian ornithology, work?
17. What are the two races of Little Green Bee-eater that are known from Egypt?
18. A weaver's nest was recently found in Sinai. Why might it not have been a Streaked Weaver which breeds in the Nile Delta?
19. Which two species of birds that breed in Egypt are designated as Globally Threatened by BirdLife International (in 1996)?
20. What species of owl breeds on the Pyramids at Siqqara?
21. Which Egyptian ornithologist recently found and described a new species of toad, endemic to the Nile Delta?
22. Whereabouts in Egypt does the Egyptian Plover now occur?
23. Which controversial figure published a book in 1930 that summarised 18th, 19th and early 20th century work on the birds of Egypt?
24. What tool does the Egyptian Vulture use to smash Ostrich eggs?
25. For which two birds with 'Senegal' in their names is Egypt the only country where they can be found in the Western Palaearctic?
26. What Globally Threatened species is regularly taken in large numbers on migration by quail-trappers in Sinai?
27. How would you separate Spotted and Lesser Spotted Eagle on their underwing pattern?

GENERAL KNOWLEDGE 1996

1. Who wrote the 'Swallows and Amazons' books in which *Coot Club* features?
2. Which Chinese owl catches crayfish by wading through the shallows at night?
3. Who wrote: *O, the honey bees are gumming*
   On their little wings, and humming
   That the summer, which is coming,
   Will be fun,
   And the cows are almost cooing,
   And the Turtle Doves are mooing…..?
4. In which year did the Collared Dove first breed in Britain?
5. What were the three categories of breeding used in the first *Atlas of Breeding Birds in Britain and Ireland*?
6. What does 'Jack' mean in Jack Snipe?
7. What is the other name for the Bald Ibis?
8. What are the three colours on an adult Goldfinch's head?
9. In the nineteenth century which British bird was reduced to just 42 pairs because of its popularity in fashionable ladies' hats?
10. Which British bird is the fastest runner, clocked at 21mph?
11. Which bird has the yolkiest egg (relative to its size)?
12. What is a gynandromorph?
13. How big an omelette would you make from the egg of an extinct Madagascar Elephant Bird (in gallons or mls)?
14. Which species has the lightest egg relative to its body weight?
15. What do European Nightjars have in common with all Hummingbirds?
16. Water sucking is unusual in birds, but pigeons are well known for doing it. Name another group that does it.
17. What is leap-frog migration?
18. Which two species of owl regularly breed in both Britain and Ireland?
19. Name one of the two 'puff-back' birds in Africa.
20. What is a Potoo?
21. Name a British parrotbill.
22. Why is the Apostle Bird so named?
23. What is the 'gobbling ground' of the Lesser Prairie Chicken?
24. By what name is the uropygial gland more popularly known?
25. To which species of bird did Linnaeus give the Latin name meaning 'bachelor finch'?

26. According to the poet William Blake, what "bird in a cage puts all Heaven in a rage"?
27. Convergent evolution has resulted in which New World species resembling the African Longclaws?
28. Where in the world would you find the Palmchat, Broad-billed Tody and Chat Tanager?
29. Where in the world would you find Couas, Vangas and Asities?
30. Which bird observatory would you be visiting if you took a boat from Port St Mary?
31. Which bird observatory would you be visiting if you took a boat from Anstruther?
32. What bird is used as the symbol of the magazine *British Birds*?
33. Which vagrant to Britain was resident on South Uist in the Western Isles between 1972 and 1984?
34. The author of *Birds of the West Indies*, who died in 1989, gave his name to a well-known fictional agent. Who was he?
35. In which extinct species of New Zealand bird did the male and female have different shaped bills?
36. Where is the largest colony of breeding Mute Swans in Britain, the site of a swannery for over 900 years?
37. What is the usual English name for the bird sometimes known as a 'Cuddy Duck', or 'St Cuthbert's Duck'?
38. In which British wader is the male considerably larger than the female?
39. When referring to young birds, what term is the opposite of altricial?
40. Which birds were at one time thought to hibernate in the mud at the bottom of ponds?
41. 'Jack and Jill' are terms sometimes used to denote the male and female of which bird?
42. Which frequent passage wader, which has exceptionally nested in Britain, uses the old nest of another species such as a thrush, crow or pigeon?

43. What species of duck takes its name from the deepest lake in the world?
44. For what bird is 'harnser' the Norfolk name?
45. The young of which bird can be most easily located by their hunger call, likened to an unoiled gate or inn-sign swinging in the wind?
46. Which British songbird regularly nests in rabbit burrows?
47. What wader is sometimes known as a 'seven whistler' after its characteristic call of about seven notes?
48. 'Goatsucker' is an old name for which British bird?
49. Julian Huxley made a classic study at Tring of the courtship behaviour of which bird?
50. Which bird's young hatch fully feathered?
51. What unique feeding method does the Lammergeier employ?
52. Which corvid is generally accepted as the species which lives at the highest altitude?
53. What is the world's most numerous bird?
54. A parliament is a collection of what?
55. What does *Archaeopteryx* mean?
56. The Resplendent Quetzal was considered sacred by which Central American Indians?
57. Which is the only native species of pheasant found in Africa?
58. What nocturnal parrot nests underground?
59. Who wrote:
    There was an old man with a beard
    Who said, 'It is just as I feared! -
    Two owls and a hen
    Four larks and a wren
    Have all built their nests in my beard.
60. Which seabird returns nocturnally to its treetop nest?
61. Who wrote:"And when you think of all those babies she's got, then all I can say is she'd better give up bird nesting - it isn't the right kind of hobby at all for a woman that can't say no even to midgets."
62. Who killed Cock Robin?
63. What with?
64. What nocturnal fruit-eating bird avoids bumping into things by using echolocation?
65. What is the easiest way of distinguishing Flying Steamer Duck from White-headed Flightless Steamer Duck?
66. Which does not habitually hover: Red-footed Falcon, Little Tern, Rough-legged Buzzard, Kingfisher, Black-winged Kite, Pallas's Warbler or Short-toed Eagle?

BIRDFAIR 1997
Mindo Important Bird Area Project

Ecuador is a tiny, developing country only slightly larger than the UK. It is home to one of the world's richest populations of birds, with more than 1,600 species. It ranks amongst the top 10 countries in the world for bird species endemism. Mindo has more than 150 species of birds, of which 6 are globally threatened. Thanks to the £60,000 raised in 1997, the Mindo Important Bird Area (IBA), the first IBA in South America, was officially launched in October 1997. The Mindo Project has heavily involved the local community and many new initiatives to learn about the special birds and their conservation have been implemented. Mindo has now become one of the most visited sites in the neotropics by birdwatchers, bringing great benefits to the local community. Several new birding lodges have been opened and more landowners are seeing the benefits of conserving the forests. The Birdfair funds have, in addition, been used to support work throughout the 200,000-hectare designated IBA, including the preparatory work for the purchase of 1,000 hectares of Polylepis forest by the Jocotoco Foundation in 2001. It also helped fund the first complete study of the natural history of the Black-breasted Puffleg, one of the world's rarest hummingbirds. During 2004, a series of workshops are planned with the local communities to assess the success of the project, and to identify priorities for future funding. Perhaps the most significant result of Birdfair funds identifying the Mindo IBA has been the creation of a US$16.9 million eco-fund for conservation work in the Mindo IBA and five other environmentally sensitive areas in the Andes.

The contestants, under the Chairmanship of Bill Oddie, were:

* Mark Avery (Royal Society for the Protection of Birds)
Richard Hearn (Wildfowl & Wetlands Trust)
David Lindo (British Trust for Ornithology)
Jane Lyons (BirdLife International)

SPECIALIST SUBJECTS 1997
Conservation of Globally Threatened Species in Europe

1. One European country officially opposes a key recommendation for preventing the extinction of a Globally Threatened species. What is this about? [1997 remember.]
2. What is the heaviest Globally Threatened species in Europe and how much does it weigh?
3. How small is the known population of the rarest of Globally Threatened species in Europe?
4. In how many countries does the most widespread Globally Threatened species occur in Europe, and what is that species?
5. How many Globally Threatened species bear the names of eminent ornithologists and naturalists, and can you name two?
6. How many of the Globally Threatened species are single country endemics?
7. Where and when was the last nest of the Slender-billed Curlew found?
8. Which European species most recently became extinct?
9. Roughly how big is the total range of the most localised European Threatened species?
10. What critical fact needs to be known to tell whether the Corncrake is really Globally Threatened?
11. How big was the estimated population of the Dark-tailed Laurel Pigeon in 1996: 800, 1,200 or 1,700?
12. What countries have breeding populations of Spanish Imperial Eagle?
13. Down which side of the Urals do almost all Red-breasted Geese migrate?
14. What kind of human interference contributed to the extinction of the White-headed Duck in France, Italy, the former Yugoslavia and Egypt?
15. The Canary Islands Houbara Bustard is found on Fuerteventura, Lobos and Lanzarote. What is the fourth island that it inhabits?
16. How often is the action plan for Pygmy Cormorant reviewed and updated by BirdLife International?
17. What were the two Globally Threatened species in Belarus in 1997?

18. What are the two main habitat protection measures being implemented to preserve the Azores Bullfinch?
19. What site remained as the only known regular wintering area for Slender-billed Curlew in Morocco (in 1997)?
20. What is the only Globally Threatened species to breed in Ireland?
21. What is the unusual aspect of the male Aquatic Warbler's behaviour that necessitates especially rich habitat for this species to breed?
22. What Globally Threatened species last bred in the UK in1832?
23. What species (which was considered to be Globally Threatened in 1997) is particularly threatened by incidental catches in lumpsucker fishery nets?
24. The scientific name for Ferruginous Duck is *Aythya nyroca*. What does *nyroca* mean?
25. What Globally Threatened species is threatened by Jamaican immigrants?
26. What is the main threat to the Greater Spotted Eagle, apart from habitat loss?
27. What was the only Globally Threatened species also known to breed in the Nearctic (in 1997)?
28. What is the name of the scheme to control the cat and rat population that threatens Zino's Petrel?
29. What is the principal threat to Audouin's Gull?
30. What nationality was Admiral Prince Heinrich Wilhelm Adalbert, after whom the Spanish Imperial Eagle is named?
31. What is the only European Globally Threatened raptor that does not breed in China?

Grey Geese of Britain and Europe

1. For which species are the Valdak Marshes an important staging ground?
2. What is the single most important factor in the huge increase of wintering Pink-footed Geese in Norfolk in recent years?
3. What is the meaning of the word 'Lag' in the name Greylag Goose?
4. The late Sir Peter Scott was the first person to recognise that the White-fronted Geese breeding in Greenland and wintering in Ireland, Western Scotland and Wales belonged to a distinctive race. To within 2 years either way, in which year was *flavirostris* formally named?

5. Excluding Lesser Whitefront, which of our grey geese on average weighs the least?
6. Which are the two main wintering sites for Bean Geese in the UK?
7. Where do the Pink-footed Geese which winter mainly in the Netherlands breed?
8. Which grey goose is protected at all times in Scotland, but may be shot in England and Wales between September and January?
9. What colour is the bill of a *rubirostris* Greylag Goose?
10. Blue phase Snow Geese are rare but regular visitors to Britain. To which subspecies do they belong?
11. Which grey goose has a distribution considered as being almost the Palaearctic equivalent of the Canada Goose?
12. Which grey goose swims more habitually than the other grey goose species in Britain and Ireland?
13. To what does the specific name of the Lesser White-fronted Goose refer?
14. How big is the native and feral population of Greylag Geese in Britain and Ireland:- 10,000-20,000, 20,000-30,000 or 30,000-40,000?

15. What species of grey goose is colloquially known as the 'laughing goose'?
16. How many geographical variations of Pink-footed Goose are there?
17. From which country do most of our Greylag Geese emanate?
18. Which 'White-front' lacks conspicuous visible 'teeth' when the bill

is closed – Lesser White-fronted Goose or White-fronted Goose?
19. Which is rarer in London – Pink-footed or White-fronted Goose?
20. Are feral Bar-headed Geese closer in size to Bean Geese or Greylag Geese?
21. Why is one grey goose in Annex 1 of the Wildlife and Countryside Act?
22. I was about to clinch the identification of a Lesser White-fronted Goose when I noticed that its closed wing projected beyond its tail. Good or bad news?
23. Who famously 'knew all the *Ansers*?'
24. Which east coast site used to be a major wintering site for Pink-footed Geese, but is no longer?
25. What trend has there been in the feeding habits of wintering White-fronted Geese?
26. What is the European breeding population of the Globally Threatened Lesser White-fronted Goose (excluding the Russian population)?
27. What is the difference, according to *Wildfowl*, between a 'wink wink' and a 'hank hank?
28. What other grey goose, apart from the Greylag, has given rise to domesticated forms?
29. What is the recommended time for roasting a goose?

Birds of London 1960-1997

1. Which London site holds the second largest heronry in Britain?
2. Curtismill Green and Denham Place have, in the 1990s, held the largest breeding colonies in the London area of which bird?
3. Who was the first birdwatcher to break the 200 species barrier in the London area in a year?
4. How large is the Inner London recording zone as defined in the London Bird Report?
5. Which wader was the only species to be added to the London list in 1995?
6. For which one of the following species are all records not required for the London Bird Report: Shelduck, Sparrowhawk, Hobby and Oystercatcher?
7. Fieldwork for the forthcoming *New Atlas of Breeding Birds of the London Area* took place between which years?
8. Which two species of gull now breed in Inner London?
9. A line drawing of which bird features on the title page of David

Montier's *Atlas of Breeding Birds of the London Area*, published in 1977?

10. Name either of the two birds lost as breeding birds in Inner London since 1965.
11. What year did Grey Herons begin breeding in Inner London?
12. What is the centre of the conventional recording area for London?
13. Which species has the largest proportion of its breeding population in London?
14. Who wrote *The Thames Transformed*?
15. Where would you be most likely to see Lesser Spotted Woodpecker in London?
16. Where did Magpies first breed away from the parks, and in what year?
17. Which site in London attracts many species not otherwise associated with Inner London?
18. Which breeding species not recorded in the first Atlas was most widespread in London in 1988-94?
19. Which seabird began nesting in London in 1991?
20. In 1995 Elmbridge Leisure Centre held the largest concentration of which noisy bird?
21. Between 1960 and 1995, how many species of owl bred in the London area?
22. Which American landbird made landfall on Barnes Common in 1984?
23. Which bird is the emblem of the London Natural History Society?
24. In which month do most Sabine's Gull records occur in London?
25. Named after a place in London, this bird has become a scarce annual vagrant in recent years. What bird is it?
26. The concrete barges on the River Thames at Rainham hold up to 30 individuals of which scarce winter passerine?
27. What invader was seen everywhere in London in 1965 and 1966?

Birds of Texas

1. You will need a cheeky answer to find Texas's only endemic breeding bird.
2. The Prairie Dog unwittingly helps which bird find a home?
3. In Texas the Olive Sparrow has another name that it shares with a Hollywood legend of yesteryear. Who was the legend?

4. Which recent invader of Texas devastated the Yellow-shouldered Blackbird on its advance north?

5. John James Audubon honoured his friend Thomas Bewick by naming which small bird after him?

6. What was Audubon's Oriole previously known as?

7. Which species of cormorant, other than Double-crested, can be found in Texas?

8. What colour are the axillaries of the Scissor-tailed Flycatcher?

9. How many species of kingfisher regularly occur in Texas?

10. Wilson's Phalarope is a regular winter visitor off the Texan coast. True or false?

11. What are the two very local passerines for which the Edwards Plateau is famous?

12. Mention "Boy Scout" to a birder in Texas and something other than Baden-Powell will probably spring to mind. What?

13. *Ajaia ajaja* is not a West Indian band but is the lovely scientific name of which locally common Texan coastal bird that is pretty difficult to misidentify?

14. Apart from bodily relief, what might a birder be particularly seeking in the rest areas on Highway 77 south from Kingsville?

15. In spring 1981 two experienced US birders claimed close views of a flock of 23 individuals of which Critically Endangered species on an island in Galveston Bay?

16. Another Critically Endangered species was recently rumoured to have been seen in Big Thicket National Preserve, although the last Texan record was around 1938. What was this species?

17. Which species is coming back from the brink of extinction in its winter stronghold at Aransas?

18. What is the National Audubon Society's list of Birds of Conservation Concern called?

19. What do 'You ain't seen nothing yet' and grassy pine woods in Texas have in common?

20. What is the state bird of Texas?

GENERAL KNOWLEDGE 1997

1. Apart from Cormorants and Shags, which other British breeding bird has webs between all four of its toes?
2. What family of birds do mynahs belong to?
3. Where would you go to look for a Kauai O-o?
4. What is the name of the joint at the end of a bird's wing to which the primary feathers are attached?
5. Which extant species has functional claws on its forelimbs?
6. What do Water Dropworts and Wheatear have in common?
7. Which two birds are always present on the roof of the City Hall in Liverpool?
8. What is a cushat?
9. Where in the world would you find Tapaculos, Puffbirds and Seedsnipes?
10. Where in the world would you find the Kakapo, Kaka and Kokako?
11. Where in the world would you find the Oos, Ou and Iiwi?
12. Which bird observatory would you be visiting if you took a boat from Baltimore?
13. What is the world's heaviest parrot?
14. Which bird has the largest communal nest?
15. Which is the most airborne bird?
16. Which bird has the slowest powered flight?
17. Which British breeding gull has only three toes (on each foot)?
18. What family of birds do tchagras belong to?
19. Where would you look for a Currawong?
20. What is the area in between the base of the upper mandible and the eye called?
21. What is the more usual name for Mother Carey's Chicken?
22. What colour is the bill of a Snow Goose?
23. If scientific names were translated literally, Black-headed Gull would not be black-headed. Which gull would be?
24. If it whoops in the Old World, what does it do in America?
25. What unique feeding technique does the Sharp-beaked Ground-Finch employ?
26. Which Club features in Arthur Ransome's *Swallows and Amazons* books?
27. To where are turkeys indigenous?
28. Which bird was the object of a 1932 campaign by the State of Western Australia to eradicate 20,000 birds using an artillery detachment?

29. Where do flyeaters meet spiderhunters?
30. What are pufflegs and sabrewings?
31. In which geological era did the first birds evolve?
32. What is the national bird of the USA?
33. Which British breeding wader has lobed feet?
34. To what family of birds do lovebirds belong?
35. Where would you go to look for a mesite?
36. Where exactly on a bird would you find the culmen?
37. What is the more usual name for Erne?
38. The puma and the snake were sacred to the Inca people. Which bird completed the trio of sacred animals?
39. Which bird lives in a cave (twice)?
40. Which British species has a wing length in millimetres about the same as ten times its weight in grams?
41. Who wrote *The Thieving Magpie*?
42. What links *Trichostrongylus tenuis* and the 12th August and why?
43. Where would a birdwatcher find Worms, Strumble and St David's Head?
44. Who wrote *The Birds*, a play first produced in 414 BC?
45. How many toes has a Sanderling?
46. When did Goldeneye first breed in Britain – 1965, 1970 or 1975?
47. What is Kentish Plover known as in the USA?
48. In Norse mythology who was the Raven god?
49. How many toes does an Ostrich have?
50. What family of birds do longclaws belong to?
51. Where would you go to look for a Cahow?
52. Where on a bird would you look for the malar stripe?
53. What is the more usual name for the Devil Bird?
54. What species was not recorded in Britain and Ireland prior to 1973, but was sufficiently common for it to be removed from the list of British rarities only 14 years later?
55. About which species did James Fisher write a New Naturalist monograph?
56. Which jazz musician was called Bird?
57. When did Snowy Owl first breed in Britain – 1967, 1972 or 1977?
58. Where was Britain's first Brown-headed Cowbird seen?
59. What are Flying Toads?
60. In the Western Palaearctic which raptor breeds only in Morocco?
61. Which bird betrayed St Stephen?
62. Where did Little Ringed Plovers first breed in Britain?
63. According to the old English proverb what "is worth the whole body of a kite"?

64. Where do most European Eleanora's Falcons go in winter?
65. What is the collective noun for Teal?
66. What other discipline might be thought to connect the Anhinga, the Egyptian Plover, *Kaupifalco monogrammicus* and the Podargidae?

BIRDFAIR 1998
Threatened Birds Programme

In 1998, 1,111 species of bird were threatened with global extinction – that is 1 in 8 of all bird species. The aim of the Threatened Birds Programme was to gather the most up-to-date information on the most threatened species, raise awareness amongst governments, decision-makers and the public of the problems these birds face and initiate action to protect them. The £120,000 raised by Birdfair allowed BirdLife to complete the mammoth task of collecting all the information on the world's globally threatened birds. This resulted in the publication of BirdLife's benchmark book Threatened Birds of the World in October 2000. A second publication, Together for Birds and People, launched at the BirdLife World Conference in 1999, was also funded by Birdfair 1998 and this reached decision-makers worldwide to alert them to the state of the birds in their regions. The globally threatened species programme has gone from strength to strength and has led to many significant targets being achieved. They include the development of the Species Module in BirdLife World Database to hold and analyse information on globally threatened birds. This information is now widely available and is included on BirdLife's website (www.birdlife.net). Through the website, the status of the world's birds can be constantly reviewed. A review, published in 2000, has resulted in a change of status of 226 species and this information was launched at the BirdLife World Conference in South Africa in March 2004. A further report was launched at the same conference - State of the World's Birds 2004.

The contestants, under the Chairmanship of Bill Oddie, were:

Dawn Balmer (British Trust for Ornithology)
Martin McGill (Wildfowl & Wetlands Trust)
* Chris Harbard (Royal Society for the Protection of Birds)
Nigel Collar (BirdLife International)

SPECIALIST SUBJECTS 1998
Ringing

1. Who is the colour ring coordinator for Cormorant in the British Isles?
2. At the end of 1995 which of the following species had been ringed in the greatest numbers in Britain and Ireland – Coot, Eider or Rock Pipit?
3. A new longevity record for Wood Warbler was recently established. To the nearest month, how old was this bird?
4. How far is the minimum control distance for Sand Martin?
5. How many birds had been ringed in Britain and Ireland by the end of 1995 - to the nearest million?
6. What is the current (1998) price for a Jap 30-foot mist-net?
7. What is the best way to sex a Greylag Goose?
8. What have Merlin, Capercaillie and Ruff got in common?
9. What is the best way of ageing a Tree Sparrow in winter?
10. What type of birds are most commonly caught in Wainwright Traps?
11. When was the *Ringers' Manual* first published by the BTO?
12. Organised bird ringing in Britain started with the independent launching of two schemes. Who by?
13. With what address were Landsborough Thomson's rings marked?
14. In which year did Witherby transfer control of his bird-ringing scheme to the BTO?
15. Which major development in the ringing scheme was initiated in 1955?
16. The first ringers' conference took place in which decade?
17. What is the EURING code for second-year birds, i.e. fledged in the previous calendar year?
18. In the early 1900s, Jack Miner in the USA marked wildfowl with rings which carried what instead of serial numbers?
19. What is the main constituent of Monel, which is the alloy used to make some rings?
20. In what year did organised ringing in Britain and Ireland start?
21. Who was the first full-time Secretary to the Ringing Committee?
22. Who is the current (1998) Chairman of the Ringing Committee?
23. What is the internal diameter of the smallest ring?
24. What is the internal diameter of the largest ring?

25. What is the most commonly ringed bird in the UK?
26. Name three of the next five most commonly ringed birds in the UK.
27. What is the species with the largest number of foreign-ringed recoveries?
28. For how long has the oldest recorded Common Tern carried its ring, to the nearest year?

Birds of Gloucestershire

1. In which year did the Peregrines at Symonds Yat first attempt to breed?
2. Which duck has established a feral population within the Forest of Dean and at other sites within the county?
3. In which year did the last recorded nesting of Red-backed Shrike occur in Gloucestershire (+/- 2)?
4. How many singing Cetti's Warblers were recorded in the county in 1996?
5. Give the year that a young Peter Scott and friends discovered two Lesser White-fronted Geese on the Dumbles, (being the 3rd and 4th records for the county)?
6. How many nest-boxes are there at the Nagshead Reserve (to the nearest 10)?
7. In which year was the first Gloucestershire Collared Pratincole found?
8. Which large bird, now well known in Gloucestershire as a winter visitor, was named after a naturalist who died two years before its discovery?
9. Name one of the two sites that Gloucestershire's first Lesser Scaup, in Nov/Dec 1994, frequented during its stay?
10. How many singing Woodlarks have been recorded in the Forest of Dean this summer (1998)?
11. Which ecological disaster started in Gloucestershire?
12. Which quacker said "howdy" in Gloucestershire in 1955?
13. When and where was the highest count of singing male Corn Buntings ever recorded in the county?
14. Who counted them?
15. Which former RSPB reserve in Gloucestershire used to hold breeding Marsh Warblers in the 1970s?
16. Which chronicler of the birds of Gloucestershire lived at The Gryphons, Cheltenham?

17. Which bird used to be known locally in Gloucestershire as 'Mumruffin' or 'Jacky-bopeep'?
18. Which vagrant to Gloucestershire, killed at Dowdeswell Wood some time before 1875, ended up being "unwillingly stuffed for a lady's hat"?
19. Which major event for ornithology in Gloucestershire took place in 1946?
20. Which species is said to have been caught in 1885 by W B Strugnell "in his soft felt hat"?
21. Which species, which would generate a major twitch nowadays, took up residence near Rectory Farm, Turkdean for over 2 months in summer 1946 before suffering the ignominy of being shot?
22. The third British record of which species was killed near Charlton Kings in October 1867?

Names of British Birds

1. Name six species on the British List with Golden in their name.
2. In which county might you find a Bilcock, a Ring Whistle and a Horner?
3. How many species on the British List have an umlaut in their name?
4. From which language is the name Grosbeak derived?
5. What is the scientific name for Saker?
6. If you went to the north of Scotland to see a Snow Fowl, what would you be seeking?
7. In the BOU list, what name is given to *Gavia adamsii*?
8. Who first named *Sylvia undata* the Dartford Warbler?
9. Which colour occurs most frequently in British vernacular bird names?
10. What are 'Yeldrocks', 'Yites' and 'Yoldrings'?
11. What British bird was known as a 'Goat Owl' in Gloucestershire and Somerset?
12. What British bird was known as 'Rattlewing' in Norfolk?
13. If a Cornishman had seen a 'Horny Wick', what species would he be talking about?
14. What is a 'Devil's Bitch'?
15. What British bird can also be called a 'Coldfinch'?
16. In Pembrokeshire what species is known as a 'Cocklolly'?
17. In Shetland an 'Ebb Cock' is a...?
18. What two species of British bird have the names of 'Pick Tarnie' in Scotland?

19. 'Cutick' is the old name used in many counties for which species?
20. What British bird was formerly known as a 'Murdering Pie'?
21. Which bird is not a catnap?
22. Which bird is named after the shape of its scapular feathers?
23. Why is a cheesy gull an example of the 'French Connection'?
24. Which bird is named after its liquid lunch?
25. Which bird has just had a dubious renaming?
26. Which bird arrives ready for cooking?
27. Which bird is hard to get undone?
28. With which bird might you have a stormy argument?
29. Which bird is liked by hunters?
30. Name three 'Pallas's' on the British List.
31. Which bird is not so smooth?
32. What Latin word is the root of the syllable 'bus' in 'bustard'?
33. What is the local name on Portland Bill for a Corn Bunting?
34. What is the local name on Portland Bill for a Wheatear?

Threatened Birds of the World

1. Which Globally Threatened wader has recently been claimed in north-east England?
2. Name three endangered species which have benefited from conservation projects in Mauritius.
3. Name the species of parrot which, following dramatic declines

due to introduced predators, has recently been translocated to predator-free islands.

4. Which Endangered Western Palaearctic passerine, thought to survive on only one island, has recently been rediscovered on Sao Nicolau?

5. In the 1990s how many Spix's Macaws were thought to exist in the wild?

6. Name the three Globally Threatened birds that occur regularly in the UK?

7. How many Bald Ibises remain in the wild in Morocco – to within 25?

8. Which bird, named after a Thai princess and known only from its wintering site, has not been seen reliably since the 1980s?

9. How many Siberian Cranes returned to Bharatpur last winter (1997-98)?

10. When and where was the last record of Crested Shelduck?

11. What British organisation is responsible for the reintroduction of the Hawaiian Goose?

12. What nocturnal scrub-inhabiting bird from eastern central India was rediscovered in 1986?

13. What *Dendroica* species breeds in jack pine woods in Michigan, USA?

14. Name the threatened *Charadrius* species that occurs in southern Western Australia.

15. What is the latest winter population estimate for the White-headed Duck?

16. On what three islands can the White-tailed Laurel Pigeon be found?

17. Name three of the main breeding population countries for Aquatic Warbler?

18. Where in the USA can a second population of Whooping Cranes be found?

19. Name two Threatened species on Martinique.

20. Which Threatened bird has the shortest common name?

21. If you were watching birds named after Archbold, Appert and Van Dam, where would you be?

22. You have heard of Ruddy Duck, but what Critically Endangered species has the name *ruddi*?

23. Name a Threatened species still to be found in the wild on Guam?

24. Many curassows, guans and chachalacas are threatened. How is this family of birds better known?

25. In terms of the scientific names, what is the odd one out of Northern Helmeted Curassow, Alagoas Curassow and Blue-billed Curassow?
26. It is no relation to the 'Mexican Wave', but the Cuban Flicker is a member of which family?
27. Vinaceous, Yellow-headed, Red-tailed and Green-cheeked are all threatened species of which type of bird?
28. Which is the only New World vulture on the threatened bird list?

GENERAL KNOWLEDGE 1998

1. What is a tiercel?
2. An unkindness of what?
3. What is a syrinx?
4. What bird appeared on the obverse of a farthing?
5. Bevy is the collective name for what?
6. What is the lightest bird in the world?
7. Where is it found?
8. Why is the generic name for Cape Pigeon or Pintado Petrel '*Daption*'?
9. What was the population of singing male Kirtland's Warbler in 1999 (give or take 100)?
10. What is the weight of an adult male Great Bustard?
11. What birds alerted the Romans on the capitol to the attacking Gauls in 390BC?
12. Birds of Paradise were originally believed to be lacking which body parts, possessed by all birds?
13. Where are the spots on a breeding Spotted Sandpiper?
14. After crossing the Red Sea the Children of Israel killed large flocks of what species of bird to ease their hunger?
15. What is the almost invariable clutch size of Hummingbirds?
16. Which species of bird has learned how to eat Ostrich eggs?

17. Why are petrels so called?
18. What do Hoopoe, Chiffchaff, and Cuckoo all have in common?
19. What is the weight of an adult male Ostrich?

20. In David's lament over Saul and Jonathan he said they were "Stronger than lions and swifter than….". Which bird?
21. Where are the spots on a Spotted Flycatcher?
22. Jemmy Twitcher was the nickname of an English Lord who had a convenience food and a bird named after him. What was the bird?
23. What adaptation does the African Harrier Hawk, or Gymnogene, possess to enable it to extract prey from holes etc?
24. What European raptor does not lay its first egg until mid-July?
25. What is the usual clutch size of the Red-billed Chough?
26. What shape are Guillemot eggs?
27. What links an Eagle, a Lark and a Treecreeper?
28. A deceit of what?
29. What is the most abundant bird in the world?
30. How many are there?
31. Where would you find a Kea?
32. What is it?
33. Why are albatrosses called *Diomedea*/Diomedidae?
34. Osprey, Ostrich, Kite, Cormorant, Hoopoe are mentioned together in Leviticus in the Old Testament. In what connection?
35. What adaptation does the Hoatzin possess for its folivorous (leaf-eating) diet that is unique among birds?
36. Where are the spots on a Spotted Crake?
37. As which bird did Jupiter seduce Leda?
38. In the Duchy of Grand Fenwick, David Kossoff found an unusual American passerine in the film *The Mouse on the Moon*. What was it?
39. In what year was the Little Owl successfully introduced into England?
40. What is the usual clutch size of the White-tailed Eagle?
41. What is the collective noun for Nightingales?
42. Who designed the London Zoo aviary?
43. A Green Woodpecker's tongue is half as long as its body. True or false?
44. A siege of what?
45. What is the most abundant wild bird in the world?
46. How many are there?
47. What is a Brown Turkey?
48. What feeding habit distinguishes Brown Pelican from all its congeners?
49. Witherby, Jourdain, Ticehurst and Tucker are collectively known for what?
50. What is the wing span of a Wandering Albatross?

51. What bird did Noah release from the Ark before he released the dove?
52. Where are the spots on a Greater Spotted Eagle?
53. The two species of seriema are named after their leg colour. What are they?
54. What large rail was rediscovered in New Zealand in 1948?
55. What was the passerine that Bernard Miles and Rosamund John got excited about in a 1944 film of the same title?
56. Who was Phoebetria after whom the Sooty Albatrosses are named?
57. What colour is a Rockhopper Penguin's eye?
58. A murder of what?
59. Which is the only British breeding bird with a white bill?
60. According to the popular song, where in London did the Nightingale sing?
61. What is a squab?
62. What is the collective noun for Choughs?
63. Who wrote the slim but instructive volumes entitled *Bird Recognition*, first published in 1947?
64. What is the longevity record of a Lesser Black-backed Gull – 34, 44 or 54 years?
65. Name three of the six types of feather.
66. What is the longevity record for a Scottish-ringed Osprey – 15, 25 or 35 years?

BIRDFAIR 1999
Rescuing Brazil's Atlantic Forests

Brazil has the second largest number of threatened birds of any country in the world. Of the 103 threatened species, 43 live in the rapidly disappearing Atlantic Forests. The main cause is habitat loss, as forests are cleared for sugar cane plantations, logging and growing crops like bananas. The forests used to extend from north-east Brazil to Argentina; now fewer than 5% of the original forest cover remains. Birdfair raised £130,000 in 1999 and, in March 2000, a Brazilian ornithologist was appointed as BirdLife's programme manager for Brazil. Three sites have been identified in the north-eastern Atlantic Forest and Birdfair support has helped to secure 2 remnant forests, Murici and Serra das Lontras. Murici is home to 13 globally threatened species and is one of the most urgent priorities for biodiversity conservation in Brazil. The Brazilian government declared Murici an ecological station in May 2001. As a result, 6,466 hectares have been given the strictest level of protection available under Brazilian law. Several critically endangered species occur in Murici and include the Seven-coloured Tanager, Alagoas Antwren, Alagoas Foliage-gleaner and the Bahia Spinetail. A plan of action for Murici was finalised in 2002. In Bahia State BirdLife has secured additional matched funding to buy nearly 500 hectares of mountain-top forest at Serra das Lontras. A portion of the forest is now being used to produce shade cacao under the cover of the existing forest canopy. It is hoped that the production of 'green' cacao will serve as an incentive for farmers to maintain and conserve adjacent forests.

The contestants, under the Chairmanship of Bill Oddie, were:

Richard Thomas (BirdLife International)
* Andy Swash (British Ornithologists' Union)
Phil Atkinson (British Trust for Ornithology)
Derek Moore (Wildlife Trusts)

SPECIALIST SUBJECTS 1999
Birds of Australia

1. What is the eye colour of a fledgling White-winged Chough?
2. All-rounder for New Zealand, but great for Aussie shorebirds. Where?
3. What bird is sometimes known as 'Tom Pudding'?
4. What is unusual about the behaviour of *Geopsittacus occidentalis*?
5. Which is the only representative of the genus *Acrocephalus* to nest in Australia?
6. What 'British' bird was introduced into Australia at Melbourne in1862?
7. Two rare parrots breed only in Tasmania but winter on the mainland. Which are they?
8. Apart from introductions, which passerine species breeds in Australia but regularly occurs in Europe?
9. Where does the Buff-breasted Paradise Kingfisher always build its nest?
10. What is the common name of the Dragoon Bird?
11. Which parrot was last recorded in Queensland in 1927?
12. What bird spectacular takes place at Roebuck Bay every spring?
13. How many flightless bird species occur in Australia and what are they?
14. Why, between 1926 and 1928, were 121,768 Emus shot and 109,345 of their eggs destroyed in Queensland?
15. Name two species of British-ringed bird that have been recovered in Australia.
16. Which species of bower bird builds the biggest bower?
17. Which one of these three bower birds always aligns its bower in a North-South axis: Tooth-billed, Satin or Spotted?
18. A colony of Banded Stilts at Lake Balee in 1980 numbered 179,000 nests. Why is this odd?
19. In the Australian soap 'Neighbours' what was the most commonly heard bird, (which had a rich fluting yodel and was often heard in Madge and Harold's garden)?
20. Which group of birds are famous for their gunshot-like calls?
21. Name two of the three avifaunal regions in Australia.
22. How many Endemic Bird Areas are there in mainland Australia?
23. Which species of pardalote is endemic to Tasmania?

24. On which toe does a Cassowary have a large claw?
25. Name three species native to Australia which regularly breed both there and in Britain.
26. Name three European species which have been successfully introduced into Australia.
27. Name two birds of paradise which are found in Australia.
28. To which family do Chowchillas, Whipbirds and Wedgebills belong?
29. What do Australian Pelican, Black-necked Stork, Comb-crested Jacana, Rainbow Bee-eater and Dollarbird have in common?
30. What colour is a female Eclectus Parrot?

Birds of Galapagos

1. How many species of Darwin's finches occur in the Galapagos?
2. Name three.
3. Which two species of owl, found commonly in the Western Palaearctic, are found on the islands as endemic races?
4. What are the three duck species that have been recorded on the islands?
5. Which endemic finch is only found on the island of Floreana?
6. Which Mockingbird is only to be found on San Cristobal?
7. Which Galapagos gull is largely nocturnal?
8. Piquero Pata Azules is Spanish for which seabird found in the islands?
9. How many main islands are there in the Galapagos?
10. No nest has yet been found in the Galapagos for one seabird, which apparently breeds on the islands. Which is it?
11. If a Waved Albatross were to fly from the most easterly point on San Cristobal to the most westerly point on the Galapagos, where would it land?
12. How far would it have flown?
13. The Waved Albatross is one of four albatross species regularly found north of the equator. Name two of the other three.
14. Why would it be appropriate for the New Zealand endemic albatross *Thalassarche eremita* (formerly considered a race of Shy Albatross) to be found breeding on San Cristobal?
15. How many species of Laridae (gulls, terns and skuas) seen in the Galapagos have also been recorded in the UK?
16. Which cuckoo species, recorded in the Galapagos, has also been seen in the UK?

17. Which resident species is known locally as the 'Canario'?
18. Why is the Woodpecker Finch unusual?
19. The Waved Albatross is endemic to the Galapagos. Where is its main breeding colony?
20. How many species of heron are resident on the Galapagos?
21. What is the ornithological significance of 'Champion Gardner'?
22. How many stages of moult do ground finches go through until they acquire adult plumage?
23. What is unusual about the Band-rumped Petrels that breed on the Galapagos?
24. What is the local name of the Galapagos Flycatcher?
25. What does the Swallow-tailed Gull make its nest from?
26. Why were large numbers of Smooth-billed Anis killed recently?
27. Name two of the four species on the front cover of A *Guide to the Birds of the Galapagos Islands* by Castro and Phillips?

Birds of the Bailiwick of Guernsey

(The Bailiwick of Guernsey is the area under the jurisdiction of Guernsey and includes Alderney, Sark, Herm, Jethou and associated islets, in addition to Guernsey, for the benefit of anyone who, like the editor, did not know that.)

1. Which species has only been seen at La Clare Mare and Rue des Bergers?
2. Who wrote *Birds of the Channel Islands*?
3. On which islands were Long-eared Owls first discovered breeding?
4. Which species, that breeds on Alderney, bred on Guernsey in 1998 for the first time?
5. What was Rue des Bergers Nature Reserve formerly called?
6. Name two American passerines recorded in the Bailiwick.
7. Who or what is Griff?
8. Who collates Guernsey Bird News?
9. What colour is Vic's hat?
10. Who is the warden of Lihou?
11. Who was the author of *Catalogue of Guernsey Birds* published in 1948?
12. In which decade was *The Birds of Guernsey and the Neighbouring Islands* by Cecil Smith published – the first book specifically on the Guernsey avifauna?
13. Who compiled *A Record of the Birds of Guernsey* published in 1950?
14. In which decade was the first of the annual ornithological reports published by La Société Guernesiaise?
15. When, to within 5 years, was the Records Committee of the Ornithological Section of La Société Guernesiaise founded?
16. Which diving bird first bred on Guernsey in1956 and remains a very irregular breeder?
17. Which seabird was first recorded on 22nd October 1967?
18. Which now regular visitor was first recorded as recently as 14th-17th May 1967?
19. The numbers of which species were augmented by introductions by the Guernsey Rabbit Shooters Association in 1975?
20. Which wildfowl species bred for the first time in 1968?
21. More than 50 of which vagrant species were recorded in late October/early November 1963?
22. Which wader occurs in Guernsey in internationally important numbers in winter?
23. In its most recent review of European Important Bird Areas, how many does BirdLife International recognise in the Bailiwick of Guernsey?
24. In BirdLife's first inventory of European Important Bird Areas only one IBA was recognised. What was it?

25. Les Etacq and Ortac are now considered as separate Important Bird Areas, but what is the third IBA recognised in the Bailiwick of Guernsey?
26. Which French 'bird' has retired to Alderney to pick up litter?
27. Which familiar British bird doesn't breed in the Bailiwick of Guernsey, but is replaced by its continental cousin there?
28. Why is it a familiar species?
29. What was the probable age and sex of the Siberian Blue Robin on Sark in October 1975?
30. Thanks to a change in the law, certain 'birds' can now keep their nest sites on Alderney. What are they?

Birds of Jordan

1. Which book, published in 1965, told the story of an ornithological expedition to Jordan?
2. Name the two Globally Threatened species breeding in Jordan.
3. A relict population of which British garden bird is resident in the Northern Highlands of Jordan – some 500 km from its nearest known neighbours?
4. Which great European rarity may still occur along the Yarmuk River in northern Jordan?
5. Who or what is the link between Gannets and Jordan?
6. When was the Azraq Wetland Reserve established?
7. Which species now resident in Aqaba is thought to have arrived there on board ship?
8. What is the only bird species known to have become extinct in Jordan in the 20th Century?
9. What is the link between a finch, a starling and 'The Land of Moab'?
10. Which species of wader is on the Western Palaearctic list solely on the basis of two records, both from the Jordan/Israel border, but 126 years apart – in 1869 and again in 1995?
11. What is the national bird of Jordan?
12. As the Sinai is actually in Egypt, why was this species chosen as the national bird of Jordan?
13. Why would the Dead Sea Sparrow *Passer moabiticus* be an appropriate choice for Jordan's national bird?
14. Who was the author of *Birds of the Hashemite Kingdom of Jordan*, published in 1995?
15. According to that book, how many species had been recorded in

Jordan until then (approximately)?

16. How many were known to have bred in Jordan (approximately)?

17. Following on from Andrews's book, who compiled the first Jordan Bird Report, covering the years 1995-1997?

18. Where was the first recorded breeding of Little Green Bee-eater in Jordan?

19. Which bird recorded in Aqaba in December 1997 was the first record of this species in the Western Palaearctic?

20. What is the earliest date that a Black-eared Wheatear has been seen in Jordan?

21. What are the two types of finch that you can see at Petra?

22. Which bird displays the orange colour of Petra as it flies?

23. Which bird first appeared in Jordan after the draining of the marshes in Southern Iraq in 1985?

24. Which common bird, named after the region, is extremely difficult to spot despite making a lot of noise?

25. Which single bird did Fares Khoury base his PhD upon?

GENERAL KNOWLEDGE 1999

1. What bird was domesticated by the Ancient Egyptians but ceased to be a domestic bird after the Persian conquest in 524 BC?
2. Which English football team is known as the Magpies?
3. What is a Yaffle?
4. What is the chief item on a Palmnut Vulture's diet?
5. What do Americans call a Shore Lark?
6. How many species of hirundine are there on the British List?
7. What is a female Black Grouse called?
8. Who called his autobiography *The Eye of the Wind*?
9. What was a 'Skunk Duck'?

10. What is *Sylvia sarda*?
11. What do Jerdon's Courser, the Cahow and the Takahe all have in common?
12. What bird did the Ancient Mariner shoot with his crossbow?
13. What quantitative adjective can be applied to Coot, Ibis, Petrel, Hummingbird and Woodrail?
14. What do landlubbers call a 'Seahen'?
15. What does the Siberian Jay's specific name *infaustus* mean?
16. What colour connects the following in Europe: Heron, Partridge, Plover and Wagtail?

17. The Nazca Booby has recently been split from the Masked Booby. Why is it called Nazca?
18. Which English football team are known as the Owls?
19. What is the chief item on a Wryneck's diet?
20. What do Americans call our Wren?
21. What sex is a tiercel?
22. When was the Madagascar Pochard last seen?
23. What was unusual about 10,000 American Coots migrating north in Oregon in May 1929?
24. What connects a Midshipman, excessive nasal mucous discharge and the Snowy Sheathbill?
25. Who wrote the play *The Seagull*?
26. In addition to *Portrait of a Wilderness* Guy Mountfort wrote two other Portrait books. Name one.
27. What is *Sylvia nana*?
28. What birds were included in the cargo of the Quinquireme of Nineveh, according to John Masefield?
29. What colour connects the following in Europe: Woodpecker, Wheatear, Kite and Guillemot?
30. What bird visited the Crimea and was awarded the Order of Merit?
31. What does the Waxwing's generic name *Bombycilla* mean?
32. What do landlubbers call a 'Sea Dove'?
33. Three football league teams are called the 'Robins'. Name one
34. What is a Water Ouzel?
35. How many species of nightjar are there on the British List?
36. What do Americans call the Great Grey Shrike?
37. The 'priolo' is a finch endemic to the Azores. What is its English common name?
38. Which extinct endemic Madagascan bird laid the largest egg ever known?
39. The sex chromosomes of a female bird are usually known by which letters?
40. What connects a subatomic particle, a low-fat cheese and the local Falkland Island name for the Black-crowned Night Heron?
41. Who was the Sheffield steel manufacturer who wrote *Birds of Siberia* in 1901?
42. What bird quoth "Nevermore", according to Edgar Allan Poe?
43. Name two US states with American warblers named after them.
44. Which one of the following is not (yet) described as Common, Eurasian, European, Northern or what have you: Bullfinch, Greenfinch, Goldfinch or Hawfinch?

45. Why is the Linnet's specific name *cannabina*?
46. What colour connects the following in Europe: Woodpecker, Sandpiper, Heron and finch?
47. What is *Sylvia deserticola*?
48. What do landlubbers call a sea turtle (the bird not the reptile)?
49. How many species of swift are there on the British List?
50. What do Americans call a Sand Martin?
51. What English football team is known as the Bantams?
52. What is the chief item in a Nutcracker's diet?
53. Raptors are anagrammatical with which other order of birds?
54. What bird married the Owl and the Pussy Cat?
55. What adjective now describes Dotterel, Sparrowhawk, Collared Dove and Wryneck?
56. Who called his autobiography *An Eye for a Bird* in 1970?
57. What was the name of the only surviving female Chatham Island Black Robin in 1979 which subsequently produced 11 young, thereby saving the species?
58. What is *Sylvia borin*?
59. What Critically Endangered black New Zealand bird is khaki (kaki)?
60. What do landlubbers call a 'Sea-parrot'?
61. What colour connects the following in Europe: Plover, Eagle, Pheasant and Oriole?
62. What role did S. Vere Benson have in ornithological education of many young (now old) birdwatchers pre-Peterson?
63. Huginn and Muninn were birds that sat on the shoulders of Odin, the god of war. What species were they?
64. In what country is Streseman's Crow endemic?
65. What is the alternative name for the alula?
66. What enigmatic African game bird was described in 1936, although suspected of existing since 1913 from a feather worn in a hat in Avakubi in the Belgian Congo?

BIRDFAIR 2000
Save the Albatross Campaign
Keeping The World's Seabirds off the Hook

Seabirds are in trouble. Recent estimates suggest that up to 300,000 are killed annually by long-line fishing hooks set deep into our oceans. Fishing boats trail out fishing lines that can be many miles long and carry thousands of baited hooks. Seabirds scavenging behind the fishing vessels try to snatch the bait as the lines are set. Many birds end up ensnared and get dragged under the water and drown. Albatrosses are the most threatened and, of the 24 species, 16 are globally threatened. Birdfair 2000 raised £122,000 for the campaign, which was launched officially at the Birdfair. In 2001, a new international treaty, the Agreement on the Conservation of Albatrosses and Petrels under the legally binding Bonn Convention, was adopted. The agreement was signed in South Africa, where BirdLife South Africa was the major beneficiary of the funds raised by the Birdfair. Nine countries have signed the Agreement, five of which have ratified it, and it came into force on 1 March 2004. Public awareness materials have been produced and distributed, including a video. In Taiwan some boats have on-board observers, or have had devices fitted. Australia and New Zealand have designated 'no fishing' areas around several islands. Already, foreign vessels fishing in New Zealand waters are heavily regulated and results indicate that the number of seabirds killed by Japanese long-liners fell from 4,000 to just 12 per year. There is much work to be done and to find out more about the campaign, visit the BirdLife website at: www.birdlife.org/actions/campaigns/save_the_albatross.

The contestants, under the Chairmanship of Bill Oddie, were:-

* Derek Moore (Wildlife Trusts)
Nigel Redman (British Ornithologists' Union)
Richard Thomas (BirdLife International)
Richard Bashford (British Trust for Ornithology)

SPECIALIST SUBJECTS 2000
Birds of Suffolk

1. What year did Avocets first return to breed in Suffolk?
2. What is a 'March Bump' better known as?
3. Whose *Catalogue of the Birds of Suffolk* (1884-1886) was the first complete avifauna for the county?
4. Two individuals of a now Critically Endangered species of wader were seen near Woodbridge in November 1852. What was the species?
5. The only clutches outside Scotland of what rare breeding duck were laid by an unmated female at Havergate Island between 1967-71. What was the species?
6. In which decade was Claud B. Ticehurst's *A History of the Birds of Suffolk* published?
7. Which rare species bred some 300 years ago at Trimley on the River Orwell, according to Sir Thomas Browne's 1682 account of birds found in Norfolk and Suffolk?
8. What links the author of the 1962 *Birds of Suffolk* (W.H. Payn) and the Moroccan race of Fulvous Babbler?
9. Where and when was Suffolk's first record of Melodious Warbler?
10. What is the peak count of breeding Lapwings at North Warren RSPB Reserve?
11. What species bred at North Warren this year for the first time for 54 years?
12. In what year was the only record of Squacco Heron at North Warren (Thorpe Fen)?
13. What is the peak count of Bean Goose (subsp. *rossicus*) at North Warren?
14. What first for Britain was recorded at Landguard in 1981?
15. What other first for Britain was present at the same time in Suffolk?
16. What is the title of the short fictionalised account by J.K. Stanford, about the return of breeding Avocets to the Suffolk coast and the attempt by a Mr Percy Warler to rob the eggs?
17. Which famous Suffolk rarity was found in November by a farmer, and subsequently seen and reported by Percy Muttitt, a game-keeper, remaining through most of December in its favoured mustard field?
18. Who is next in this sequence: Bert Axell, Jeremy Sorensen, ...?

19. 12th October 1995 saw 2 different individuals of this North American bird found in Suffolk, at Thorpeness Common and Southwold, doubling the previous county total. What was it?
20. The last Suffolk nest of which species was found in a rye field at Icklingham in 1832?
21. Which species on the British list on the basis of a single individual caught on a boat nearly a hundred years ago has been variously claimed by both Suffolk and Norfolk?
22. What race of North American sparrow breeds only on Sable Island and is named after a town in Massachusetts and not after a town in Suffolk?
23. In 1985, a Greater Yellowlegs at Minsmere flew off, but what rare wader then flew in to the reserve?
24. What scarce migrant did Reg hear singing when he was sitting on the toilet at Minsmere?

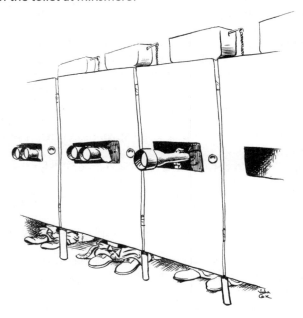

25. Who found the Red-eyed Vireo at Lowestoft?
26. What is the connection between Suffolk's first record of Red-footed Falcon and the Blaydon Races?
27. For a bonus point, sing the first lines of the Blaydon Races.
28. Prior to their recolonisation of Suffolk, when did Avocets last breed in Suffolk?

Birds of Morocco

1. When was the first confirmed breeding of Red-crested Pochard in Morocco?
2. Where was the first winter record of a Red-breasted Flycatcher in Morocco (in 1992)?
3. When was the only recent breeding of Ferruginous Duck in Morocco?
4. When was the last breeding pair of Spanish Imperial Eagles in Morocco?
5. How many Northern Bald Ibises mysteriously died in an apparent poisoning outbreak in 1996?
6. Which widespread tropical African bird is represented in Morocco by the endemic race *ayesha*?
7. How does the male of the Northwest African race of Northern Wheatear 'Seebohm's Wheatear' *O. o. seebohmi* most obviously differ from the nominate race?
8. To within one either way, how many species of lark breed in Morocco?
9. What do the following have in common: Yasmina, Les Etoiles de Dune, Sud and Dunes d'Or?
10. Which species of gamebird appears to have become extinct in Morocco in the early 1970s?
11. Of which globally threatened species does most of the remaining world population breed on seacliffs on the Moroccan Atlantic coast?
12. Which Northwest African endemic is named after a surgeon with the French Foreign Legion who collected the specimens from which it was described in 1852?
13. What do Double-spurred Francolin, Dark Chanting Goshawk and African Marsh Owl have in common?
14. What year was the last confirmed sighting of Demoiselle Crane in Morocco?
15. Ouarzazate lake is one of the top inland birdwatching sites in southern Morocco. Spell it.
16. Which species was recorded in Morocco in 1995, supplying the only accepted Western Palaearctic record?
17. Which species of wildfowl was added to the Western Palaearctic list thanks to a 1984 sighting in Morocco?
18. Name the subspecies of White Wagtail in Morocco.
19. To within one either way how many species of wheatear breed in Morocco?

20. The mountain species *Rhodopechys sanguinea* is found in Morocco. What is its English name?
21. *Sitta europaea* is found in Morocco. True or false?
22. *Picus vaillantii* is found in Morocco. What is its English name?
23. What much sought-after species is associated with the Tagdilt track?
24. Which hirundine is only known from Morocco in the Western Palaearctic?
25. What seems to have disappeared from Igoudar in recent years?
26. Which two species of raptor that occur in Africa, breed only in Morocco?
27. Name the race of Crimson-winged Finch found in Morocco.
28. What bird were Steve Whitehouse and others looking for in the Atlas Mountains when they were chased by armed bandits?
29. Who drove the getaway car so brilliantly on this occasion that the bandits were unable to block off their escape?
30. On a Moroccan birdwatching trip, why were Phil Hurrell and his companions stopped from camping on an apparently suitable piece of grass?
31. What did Phil Hurrell and companions do when they were woken up in the middle of the night by a somewhat annoyed Moroccan soldier?
32. Merdja Zerga is famous for what?

British Rarities of the 1980s

1. The Duchess of York comes from Dummer, Hants. Why did hordes of twitchers once descend there as darkness fell?
2. A much sought-after rarity was killed by a Sparrowhawk in 1984. What was it?
3. What could have caused a sand dance around Portland Lighthouse in June 1984?
4. What passerine took ten years after its discovery to be accepted to the British List and then only because a second turned up?
5. What did Bill Oddie find on the Out Skerries in October 1983?
6. The first White-throated Robin for Britain occurred on 22nd June 1983. Where?
7. Midhope Moor produced one of the shocks of the decade. What was it?
8. How many Red-footed Falcons were accepted in Britain in 1989?

9. What was the rarity connection between Tresco, Aber and North Kessock in the early 1980s?

10. A drake Steller's Eider on South Uist which first appeared in May 1972 was a popular object of pilgrimage by birders during its long stay. In which year did it finally disappear?

11. Which species led birders a merry dance round the lanes of East Dorset and West Hampshire over New Year 1988, and was famously captured on film by a lucky television crew?

12. Which rarity bred in Cambridgeshire, unsuccessfully, in 1983, and in Norfolk in 1987, successfully fledging 2 young?

13. The last record in Britain of this beautiful wader was from 29th September to 2nd October 1984 on Hadleigh Marsh in Essex. What was it?

14. The first British record of this wader occurred on 15th September 1989 at Scatness and Pool of Virkie, Shetland. What species?

15. Blacktoft RSPB reserve remarkably had two British firsts in the 1980s. What were they?

16. Which wader has occurred twice only in Britain, on both occasions in the 1980s from late August into early September?

17. Which American passerine which turned up in west Cornwall in November 1982 for the only time was a leucistic individual?

18. Which species which occurred in the 1980s holds the record long stay for an American passerine, though it often proved remarkably elusive during its stay?

19. In late November 1982, which two rare herons were seen on the same day on Humberside?

20. Name the gravel pits where the 1980 Sooty Tern was found.

21. Which year was Elsie the Lesser Crested Tern first seen on the Farne Islands?

22. Which first for Europe was given a helicopter ride to Suffolk in 1981?

23. Which two hirundines were added to the British list during the 1980s?

24. How many Olivaceous Warblers were recorded in Britain in the 1980s?

25. What first for Britain was suppressed by the RSPB?

26. What surprised Steve Gantlett on a Sunday morning in June on the Norfolk coast?

27. Which two rarities turned up within a few days and a few miles of each other in late January 1980 in Dorset at Radipole and Portland, respectively?

28. Sussex played host to two long-staying rare crakes in 1985, in March and from October to December respectively. What species and where?
29. A first for Britain, that spent four months in East Anglia in 1981, was originally misidentified. What was it originally thought to be?
30. Which two British firsts, in 1985 and 1988, both from America, were found by the same observer?

Bedfordshire's Birds

Before questions start, tell the audience: 'Bedfordshire' is a long word, so the word 'Beds' is used throughout, to save time when the questions are asked. The joke about 'Birds in Beds' is an old one. Please do not spoil the contestant's chances by sniggering. Sandy, Beds, is of course also a well-known very uncomfortable place.

1. What bird is depicted on the logo of the Beds Bird Club?
2. How many Caspian Terns have occurred in Beds?
3. Who was responsible for getting Yellow-billed Cuckoo added to the Beds List?
4. Which wader first bred in Beds in 1997 and has nested every year since?
5. What perched on gravestones and on the church at Shillington on the evening of 24th January 1958?
6. Which species returned to breed regularly in Beds in 1995, after a 100-year absence?
7. There were tetrad breeding bird surveys in 1968-77 and 1988-92. The second-largest range expansion between the two surveys was a 39% increase by Great Spotted Woodpecker. But which species increased its range by a massive 47%?
8. And, between those two surveys, which species' range contracted the most, by 44%?
9. Which make of car do you associate with breeding Black Redstarts in Beds in 1972, 1973 and 1974?
10. Which resident passerine, with 7,000-21,000 pairs breeding in Britain, has not been seen in Beds for just over 100 years?
11. Which long-awaited addition to the Beds list burst upon the county in 1997, with at least seven individuals?
12. Where is the only regular breeding site for Water Rails in Beds?
13. Up to 70 individuals of which introduced species occurs in winter and spring at Stockgrove Country Park?

14. Black-necked and Slavonian Grebes have occurred in Beds in almost every month. But which – by far – is the favoured month?
15. At which locality have feral Whooper Swans bred successfully, feral Goldeneyes failed to breed in nest boxes, and Ring-necked Duck and Red-crested Pochard both been trapped?
16. Which of these species has NOT been seen in Beds: Pallas's Sandgrouse, Sabine's Gull, Collared Pratincole, Subalpine Warbler, Barred Warbler or Sharp-tailed Sandpiper?
17. Which species, now extinct as a breeding bird in Beds, last bred, rearing three young, at Blue Lagoon, Arlesey, in 1975?
18. Finch flocks are much smaller now than formerly. By far the largest flock of a single species was one of 4,000 in 1962. What species?
19. The first nesting of Little Ringed Plovers in Beds was in 1951. Did (Common) Ringed Plovers first start to breed regularly in 1941, 1961 or 1971?
20. Which species was introduced to Beds in about 1890, was 'admitted' in 1971, and was censused in 1997-99?
21. Which passerine has been seen in Beds only once, in a garden at Mountfield Road, Luton, on 28th May 1987?
22. Name three of the four species of North American wader seen in Beds.
23. How large was the largest 20th-century flock of Bohemian Waxwings seen in Beds: 5, 35 or 65?
24. There were only two records of singles of this duck before 1944, but it first bred in Beds in 1982, and 200 occurred in November-December 1986. Which species?
25. With only three records (at Fenlake, at Stewartby and on the A507 Clifton By-pass), which is the rarest auk in Beds?
26. Not added to the county list until 1997, which is the rarest skua in Beds?
27. After a party of three at Renhold in 1916, it was a further 80 years before the next, a first-winter at Rookery Clay-pit on 1st-2nd October 1996. What species?
28. Which British-breeding passerine has occurred only twice in Beds, at Cockayne Hatley and Blows Downs?
29. After being extremely rare for over 40 years, which raptor has occurred annually in autumn and winter since the mid 1990s?
30. Where is the most favoured locality for migrant Ring Ouzels in Beds?

GENERAL KNOWLEDGE 2000

1. What is a stormcock?
2. When was the BTO founded?
3. What bird is reputed to say 'wet my lips'?
4. Where is the blue on a Blue Tit?
5. What is the principal food of the Short-toed Eagle?
6. In what year did the British Birdwatching Fair support Halmahera?
7. And what was the flagship species?
8. What is a Mountain Chicken?
9. Which of the following ovenbirds does not exist? Canebrake Groundcreeper, Buff-browed Cliffcreeper, Sharp-tailed Streamcreeper or Point-tailed Palmcreeper?
10. How can you distinguish a male from a female (Common) Starling in all seasons?
11. What is a Paddy or Snotty?
12. When was Rutland Water Nature Reserve created?
13. Sir Ernest Shackleton and the crew of the James Caird consumed the chicks of which bird on arrival at South Georgia after their epic boat journey in May 1916?
14. What romance for violin and orchestra did Vaughan Williams write concerning a now declining farmland species?
15. What bird is the logo of the BTO?
16. Martha died in Cincinnati Zoo on 1st September 1914 – the last of her kind. What species was she?
17. Where is the allantois to be found?
18. What bird is reputed to say 'Quick, Doctor, Quick'?
19. What bird is on the logo of the BOU?
20. What is a 'Mavis'?
21. What are the 'Green Linnets'?
22. Where is the white on a breeding Black Guillemot?
23. What is the connection between President Lyndon Baines Johnson and dull brown passerines?
24. What is the principal food of Verreaux's Eagle?
25. Which of the following ovenbirds does not exist? Firewood Gatherer, Greythroated Leaf-tosser, Henna-hooded Foliage-gleaner or Green-winged Compost-maker?
26. In what year did the British Birdwatching Fair support the Spanish Steppes?
27. And what was the flagship species?

28. Rutland Water is the most important wintering site in Britain for which species of duck?
29. The opera *La Gazza Ladra* by Rossini features which bird?
30. How can you distinguish a male from a female Great Tit?
31. What does *Phylloscopus* literally mean?
32. When was the BOU founded?
33. What is another name for a bird's furcula?
34. Where is the gold on a Goldfinch?
35. What is a 'Stinker'?

36. When were Ospreys first translocated to Rutland Water?
37. When was BirdLife founded?
38. What bird is said to say "A little bit of bread and no cheese"?
39. Which of the following ovenbirds doesn't exist? Plain Woodhaunter, Striped Woodhaunter, Straight-billed Reedhaunter or Curve-billed Reedhaunter?
40. What is a Bombay Duck?
41. In what year did the British Birdwatching Fair support Vietnam?
42. And what was the flagship species?
43. How can you distinguish a male from a female Common Kingfisher?

44. What is the chief food of the Hook-billed Kite?
45. Which critically endangered parrot depends on the Wax Palm (*Ceroxylon quindiuense*), Colombia's national tree, for nesting, feeding and roosting?
46. What species of albatross has nested on Taiaroa Head on South Island of New Zealand since about 1919?
47. What is a 'Merle'?
48. Incas died in Cincinnati Zoo on 21 or 28 February 1918 – probably the last of his kind. What species was he?
49. What is the BirdLife International logo?
50. What ballet did Tchaikovsky write about a large waterbird?
51. What African bird family possesses pigments to produce red and green coloration that occur in no other families?
52. What is a mollymawk?
53. In what year did the British Birdwatching Fair support Brazil's Atlantic Rainforests?
54. And what was the flagship species?
55. Where is the red knob on a Red-knobbed Coot?
56. For what species of hirundine do Americans erect an amazing variety of nest boxes?
57. When was the Wildlife Trusts' partnership formed?
58. What bird is reputed to say "I am the Red-eyed Dove"?
59. Which of the following ovenbirds does not exist? Chestnut-throated Spinetail, Black-throated Thistletail, Blue-throated Prickletail or White-throated Barbtail?
60. What is a Grand Eagle?
61. How many species have been recorded at Rutland Water?
62. How can you distinguish a male from a female Green Woodpecker?
63. Tchaikovsky wrote a suite about a dining implement although ornithologists think it was about a member of the crow family. What was it?
64. What is the principal food of the Lammergeier?
65. What is the most southern European country in which the Common Guillemot breeds?
66. What is the Wildlife Trusts logo?

BIRDFAIR 2001
Eastern Cuba:
Saving a Unique Caribbean Wilderness

Cuba is the largest island in the Caribbean with more than 350 species of birds, of which 25 are endemic. The unique wildlife of Cuba is threatened by habitat loss from conversion to agriculture, cattle ranching, urban development, lumber production and mining. This loss of habitat has already resulted in 15 species of birds being recognised as globally threatened. Fortunately, Cuba's record of establishing protected areas is exemplary as it already has 81 nationally important protected areas, including 8 natural, 14 national and 6 biosphere reserves. The 2001 Birdfair raised £135,000, which was used by many of the institutions involved in the project to purchase computers, field equipment such as binoculars, GIS systems and recorders. Remote biological stations in protected areas have already received solar panel modules to help generate power to operate this equipment. In January 2004, the first IBA conference took place in the province of Santu Espiritu. At this conference, 35 potential IBAs were officially recognised with the vast majority being in the Eastern portion of the country where the strongholds for several of the globally threatened birds occur. The five partner organisations involved in the project will begin fieldwork in 2004, using a 4x4 vehicle purchased with Birdfair money, and will visit little known areas including the Humboldt National Park. This was the last known area where the Ivory-billed Woodpecker was seen in the mid-1980s.

The contestants, under the Chairmanship of Chris Packham, were:-

* David Gandy (BirdLife International)
Rob Robinson (British Trust for Ornithology)
James Robinson (Wildfowl & Wetlands Trust)
André Farrar (Royal Society for the Protection of Birds)

SPECIALIST SUBJECTS 2001
Twitching in the UK 1985-1995

1. Which bird caused chaos on the North Norfolk coast road on August Bank Holiday 1985?
2. The Cedar Waxwing in Nottingham in 1996 sparked enormous interest, while the first, 11 years earlier, had been placed in category D because of the possibility that it was an escape. Where was this record, now accepted as the first for Britain?
3. A pair of Slender-billed Gulls at Cley in May 1987 was a big draw. When was the most recent of the previous records?
4. In which year was the first Lesser Scaup recorded in Britain?
5. When and where was Britain's first Moussier's Redstart recorded?
6. Why might you have got a call in the middle of the night requesting your presence at Tynemouth during July in the early nineties?
7. What histrionics lasted from 6 February to 17 May 1991 on the Wick River?
8. Three immature males of this species spent 11 days in February 1987 in rape fields at Hill Farm, Theberton in Suffolk – what were they?
9. Which warbler was the first for mainland Britain in 1992, turning up at Holme in August?
10. Why will Winspit in Dorset always be held in affection by birders?
11. On what island was Britain's first Philadelphia Vireo recorded in 1987?
12. What other vireo was added to the British list between 1985-1995?
13. Which crowd-pulling first for Britain was found in a mistnet in Greater Manchester in March 1994?
14. Which wader on Scilly in 21st May 1988 was the first UK record of its species for 98 years?
15. How many species did BOURC add to the British & Irish List during 1985-95, to the nearest five?
16. *Oenanthe pleschanka* is the scientific name of which rarity recorded almost annually in Britain?
17. At which site in North Humberside did the Mugimaki Flycatcher turn up in November 1991?
18. Which single-observer first for Britain was caught on video at Lands End on 1 October 1995?
19. In early July 1989, news broke of a Brünnich's Guillemot on the cliffs at Sumburgh Head in Shetland. Which mega-rarity was a

popular draw in southeast Yorkshire at the same time?

20. Two American firsts for Britain in 1989 each drew crowds of thousands – the first in Kent in February and the second in Norfolk in October. What were they?

21. What spent from 22 July to 6 August 1990 on Pilling Marsh, Lancashire?

22. The second Hooded Warbler for Britain was recorded in 1992 on which island?

23. In autumn 1990, American birds were found dead at both the Wildfowl & Wetlands Trust's HQ in Slimbridge and the RSPB's at Sandy. What were they?

24. When and where was the first Chestnut-sided Warbler recorded in Britain?

25. Which American wood warbler was first recorded in Britain at Rame Head, Cornwall in 1985?

26. What species added extra value to a sponsored birdwatch on Shetland on 19 May 1990?

27. What is the Spanish for Pallas's Sandgrouse?

28. When did Pete Ellis find the first British Great Knot in Shetland?

29. 24 May 1992 was a frustrating day for many birders with attention split between Cambridgeshire and Yorkshire – what were the species involved?

30. The first Blackpoll Warbler to reach the east coast of Britain was recorded in 1993 at which site?

British Seabirds

1. What is 'climming'?
2. When was the Great Auk lost to the world?
3. Which British seabird occupies its breeding site for the longest period of the year?
4. What is the smallest British seabird?
5. Where would the men of the Parish of Ness on Lewis go to get the gugas?
6. In which year was the Torrey Canyon oil disaster?
7. What is the scientific name for Leach's Storm-Petrel?
8. What is the derivation of the name Gannet?
9. In which year was the first Sandwich Tern collected at Sandwich?
10. How long does it take a Bonxie chick to fledge?
11. What is the commonest auk in the Atlantic?
12. How many colonies of Gannets are there in Britain?
13. What does the abbreviation AOT mean?
14. Where are the world's three main breeding colonies of Great Shearwaters? Name two.
15. For a bonus name the third.
16. Where do the most northerly Roseate Terns regularly nest?
17. Until the late 1800s, where was the only known colony of Fulmars in Britain?
18. In which year was the first recorded breeding attempt of Mediterranean Gull in Britain?
19. What is the typical weight of a Tystie?
20. What percentage of the world's population of Manx Shearwaters breeds in British and Irish colonies?
21. Where is the largest breeding colony of Tysties in the UK?
22. Where is the biggest Bonxie colony?
23. Shag regularly breeds on the RSPB reserve at Coquet Island: true or false?
24. How many Leach's Storm-Petrels were estimated to be wrecked in Bridgewater Bay during the gales of 21 October and 8 November 1952?
25. What is the Italian name for Razorbill?
26. Name our two seabirds with truly circumpolar breeding distribution.
27. In which decade of which century were Common, Roseate and Arctic Terns fully distinguished and described?
28. When did Tystie become extinct as a breeding bird in Yorkshire?

Terns of Europe

1. What is the most numerous breeding species of marsh tern in Europe?
2. Where is the closest site of regular breeding by Sooty Terns to mainland Europe?
3. Which tern would you associate with the Magic Roundabout?
4. Name a species of tern that shows a winter head pattern in autumn after a post-breeding season moult.
5. What is the world's largest tern?
6. List the three *Chlidonias* terns in decreasing order of size
7. Aleutian Tern was recorded in Europe for the first time in 1979. Why did North American birders find this so remarkable?
8. Roughly how far from its breeding grounds was the 1979 Aleutian Tern in Northumberland (to the nearest 1,000km)?
9. When was the first record of Brown Noddy in Norway?
10. What is the incubation period for Whiskered Tern eggs?
11. What is the most numerous species of European tern?
12. How many species of tern have been recorded in a wild state in Europe, but not in Britain and Ireland?
13. What is the typical length of a Caspian Tern's bill?
14. What is the scientific name for Gull-billed Tern?
15. Which species of tern, once recorded at Rutland Water, was nicknamed 'Sterna letsbehavinyoufranco'?
16. How many species of tern breeding in Europe have got black legs?
17. Describe or make the characteristic call of a Caspian Tern.
18. Which New World tern was recorded for the first time in north-west Europe during the 1990s but has not made it onto the European list?
19. The name of which brand of lager contains the initials of the six commonest British terns, plus those of three more European species?
20. What length does the tail of an adult Roseate Tern grow to?
21. With the exception of extralimitals, such as Elegant and Lesser Crested, which tern breeds in the fewest European countries?
22. What is the most northerly nesting 'crested' tern?
23. What is the name for the Little Tern in Italian?
24. Where do Elegant Terns breed?
25. Which population of Lesser Crested Terns has longer wings – Mediterranean or Red Sea?
26. What does *Gelochelidon* literally mean?

Birds of the Estuaries of North-West England

1. In North-west England, are there more sites supporting internationally important numbers of Black-tailed or Bar-tailed Godwits?
2. The massive count of 110,000 Wigeon at the Ribble Estuary during the 1994-95 winter was the second-highest ever recorded in Europe. In which country was the highest site count made?
3. How many Pink-footed Geese were thought to be present in south-west Lancashire in October 1999 (to the nearest 5,000)?
4. Which species of goose occurred in flocks of several thousands at the Dee Estuary until the end of the 19th Century, occurring in much lower numbers in recent years?
5. In which year did WWT purchase Martin Mere?
6. Is the Duddon Estuary an SPA?
7. How many Shelducks were recorded on the Ribble Estuary in the 1994-95 winter WeBS count (to the nearest 500)?
8. Which winters in greater numbers on the Dee Estuary - Knot or Dunlin?
9. Between 1996 and 1999, which winter has seen the highest counts of Knot at Morecambe Bay?
10. What was the highest single WeBS count of Little Egrets at a north-west site in the 1990s?
11. What is the only species of wildfowl wintering at the Alt Estuary in nationally important numbers?
12. How many Turnstones were counted during WeBS Core Counts on the Mersey in December 1999 (to the nearest 100)?
13. To the nearest 1,000 hectares, how large is Morecambe Bay?
14. The east Hoyle Bank is an important feeding area for waders in which estuary?
15. Name three wader species for which the Solway Firth is of international importance.
16. For a bonus name three more.
17. How many bird species is the Solway Firth internationally important for in total?
18. The Mersey Estuary is nationally important for Red-breasted Merganser: true or false?
19. How many estuaries in NW England, included in WeBS counts, are internationally important for Grey Plover?

20. Which is the most ubiquitous wader on north-western estuaries, occurring on the highest proportion of WeBS low-tide count sections?
21. How many Brent Geese were present in north-west England in January 2000 (to the nearest 10)?
22. Which three waterfowl species is the Mersey Estuary internationally important for?
23. Hodbarrow Lagoon is a key high-tide roost for terns in which estuary?
24. Is Sanderling listed as a qualifying species for the Mersey Estuary SPA?
25. The proposed SPA Mersey Narrows and North Wirral Foreshore has been identified as nationally important for which two breeding species?
26. What is the least rare species of wader on the British List yet to be recorded in north-west England?
27. What is the scientific name for Ringed Plover?

GENERAL KNOWLEDGE 2001

1. What do we all have to call the Common Gull now?
2. What species frequently roosts in depressions in the bark of Wellingtonia?
3. Why is the Bulo Burti Boubou – *Laniarius liberatus* – called *'liberatus'*?
4. What IUCN Red List category comes between Vulnerable and Critically Endangered?
5. In what country is Cobb's Wren endemic?
6. In what IUCN Red List category is the Cuban Macaw?
7. In what year did the British Birdwatching Fair support Poland?
8. And what was the flagship species?
9. Although the average Long-tailed Tit's nest contains 1,500 feathers, what is the maximum number that has been laboriously counted in a single nest (to the nearest 100)?
10. How many breeding pairs of Black-browed Albatrosses did the November 2000 census in the Falkland Islands reveal (to the nearest 20,000)?
11. The decline of the Falkland Black-browed Albatross breeding population by 86,000 in 5 years is thought to be largely due to what cause?
12. Which of the following species does not exist? Oahu Oo, Ooaa, Hihi or Hoho?
13. What bird quoth "Nevermore" according to Edgar Allen Poe?
14. It is a 'Bog Drum' in Ireland, a 'Bog Bumper' in Scotland and a 'Butterbump' in Yorkshire. What is it?
15. Who illustrated *The Birds of America* between 1827-1838?
16. What is the ornithological title of the romantic melodrama starring Elizabeth Taylor as a beatnik artist and Richard Burton as a minister?
17. What is the world population of the Alaotra Grebe thought to be?
18. What do Americans call the Grey Phalarope?
19. Why was there no Wildfowl Count in March 2001?
20. Who designs the posters for the British Birdwatching Fair?
21. In which country is the Pink Pigeon endemic?
22. BirdLife Malta recently censused the number of bird-trapping sites on Malta and Gozo. What was the total (to the nearest 100)?
23. What critically endangered North American warbler, last seen in 1988, winters (wintered?) in Cuba?

24. Who was the senior editor of *Birds of the Western Palaearctic* (until his death on 20 August 1987)?
25. The scientific name for the Laysan Albatross is *Phoebastria* (formerly *Diomedea*) *immutabilis*. Why '*immutabilis*'?
26. Which of the following does not exist? Grey Flycatcher, Drab Flycatcher, Dull Flycatcher or Leaden Flycatcher?
27. On the Lake Isle of Innisfree W.B. Yeats's evenings were going to be full of what bird's wings?
28. In what year did the British Birdwatching Fair support the Danube Delta?
29. And what was the flagship species?
30. What do the Hoatzin, Limpkin, Sunbittern, and Ibisbill all have in common?
31. What common name is applied to both the Black-capped Petrel and the Oilbird?
32. What relatively uncommon British passerine has recently been discovered feeding in Breckland stubble-fields?
33. What flying Pacific seabird frequently rolls its egg many metres from the original 'nest' during incubation?

34. Name 3 of the six types of feather.
35. What do Americans call the Arctic Skua?
36. What species of bird, in the wild, on 31 August, has the largest biomass in Britain?
37. What does *Campephilus principalis* have to do with the Bird Fair?
38. Who was the first person ever to ring an Osprey chick in England?
39. In what country is the Kagu endemic?
40. Which of the following species does not exist? Black-spectacled Tanager, Black-eared Tanager, Black-goggled Tanager or Black-faced Tanager?

41. What was the single topic to which the August 1962 edition of *British Birds* was devoted, which resulted in extensive revision of early twentieth century rarity records?
42. And who was the taxidermist at the centre of the Hastings Rarities?
43. In what year did the British Birdwatching Fair support Ecuador?
44. And what was the flagship species?
45. How many contour feathers does a Ruby-throated Hummingbird have (to the nearest 100)?
46. Why is the Admiralty Monarch – *Monarcha infelix* – called '*infelix*'?
47. What organ was used by taxonomists to distinguish oscine from suboscine passerines?
48. What species rears one young every 3 or 4 years on Macquarie Island, said to be the lowest breeding rate for any bird species?
49. Who was the ornithologist, artist and doctor who died with Captain Scott returning from the South Pole?
50. Who were the authors of the classic *Collins Field Guide to the Birds of Britain and Europe*, first published in 1954?
51. What do the Kakapo, Great Snipe, Great Bustard, and Jackson's Whydah all use in their display?
52. As what bird did W.C. Fields refer to Mae West in a film of the same name?
53. In addition to two Owls, a Hen and four Larks what other bird had made its nest in the beard of Edward Lear's *Old Man with a Beard*?
54. On 25 May 2001 a gamekeeper in Morayshire was convicted and fined £2,000 for shooting a particular bird of prey – the first ever such conviction. What was the bird of prey?
55. Zino's Petrel only breeds on one island in the world (as far as is known). Which is it?
56. And how many pairs bred in 2000 (plus or minus 20%)?
57. What critically endangered Cuban raptor was recently seen for the first time since 1992?
58. What year did the British Birdwatching Fair support the Save the Albatross Campaign?
59. What was the flagship species?
60. What sort of bird is a 'Flat-chested Urumutum'?
61. Which of the following does not exist? Sad Flycatcher, Squalid Flycatcher, Sordid Flycatcher or Stolid Flycatcher?
62. What is the common name for *Garrulax konkakinhensis* (recently discovered in Vietnam)?
63. Why is the Long-tailed Shrike – *Lanius schach* – called '*schach*'?
64. Who was the Cheshire-born artist who lived latterly in Anglesey

until his death in 1979, and who was famous for his measured drawings?
65. How many contour feathers does a Bald Eagle have (to the nearest 1000)?
66. What northern pelagic seabird was discovered breeding on Dyer Island off Cape Province in 1977?

BIRDFAIR 2002
Saving the Last Lowland Rainforests in Sumatra

Sumatra's lowland rainforests are disappearing fast, and many of the spectacular birds that depend on them face extinction. The causes of the forest destruction include political upheaval in Indonesia, and investment and purchasing decisions made by European companies and consumers. However, innovative action by local groups in Sumatra has shown that local people care about the future of their rainforests and that the situation is not hopeless. The World Bank predicted that virtually all of Sumatra's rainforests would be lost by 2005 if the present rate of logging continued. The £147,000 raised by Birdfair 2002 has helped BirdLife Indonesia to undertake surveys and consultations to prepare the feasibility study for the Sumatra Initiative. BirdLife is working with the Directorate General of Forest Production to redesign and restructure forest areas in Jambi and South Sumatra. The result of the agreement will allow a production forest, previously scheduled for logging, to be managed with the main objective of conservation. BirdLife International is working with government organisations to develop an appropriate policy for ecosystem restoration that will accommodate the Sumatra Initiative. A foundation is being established to hold the concession and, once the foundation has been established, the BirdLife partnership will seek additional funding to support the long-term future of BirdLife reserve management in Sumatra.

The contestants, under the Chairmanship of Bill Oddie, were:-

* Richard Thomas (Oriental Bird Club)
Callan Cohen (African Bird Club)
Keith Betton (Ornithological Society of the Middle East)
Andy Mitchell (Neotropical Bird Club)

SPECIALIST SUBJECTS 2002
British and Irish Twitching 1980 -1989

1. Four new species for the British List were first seen in Wales in the 1980s. Name two of them.
2. What first for Britain and Ireland was found at Ballycotton, Co. Cork, on 7 February 1981?
3. On today's date (17 August) in 1989, what species was discovered at Great Wakering in Essex?
4. In May 1982 a warbler overshot its Mediterranean breeding grounds and stopped in South Yorkshire. It was a first. Name it.
5. The second record of this raptor was a bird found dead in a Humberside cabbage patch in 1981. What was it?
6. On 3 August 1988 a storm-petrel seen off Cornwall was subsequently re-identified as Matsudaira's Storm-petrel, but what was the original identification?
7. A first for Britain and Ireland in 1988 was Crag Martin. What was unusual about this?
8. In April 1982, Ipswich moved to Dorset. Explain.
9. Which species, first seen in Britain in Falmouth Bay in February 1980, had clocked up 17 sightings by 1989?
10. What surprising raptor was seen in June 1985 on South Uist during a Corncrake survey?
11. Which British first for 93 years was observed in a drainage ditch in Stone Creek, Humberside in May 1982 accompanied by a Great White Egret?
12. When was the next one seen?
13. Name three species that were added to the British List having been seen in 1989.
14. In 1989 a Double-crested Cormorant appeared at Billingham, Co. Durham. How many days did it stay?
15. In which year was there a record influx of White-rumped Sandpipers?
16. September 1985 and Tony Soper had a funny tern on TV. What species and where?
17. 1985 produced two American wood-warblers that were firsts for Britain. What were they?
18. All except one of the following were also firsts in 1985 – Grey Catbird, Indigo Bunting, Daurian Starling and Brown Shrike. Which was not?

19. Where did the first Grey Catbird appear in 1986?
20. 1983 produced, in addition to Alpine Swift, two other rare swifts. Name one.
21. Two mega rarities appeared at Cliffe in Kent in the 1980s – what were they?
22. In which year was there a record influx of Red-rumped Swallows?
23. On 30, 31 August and 1 September 1982 you had a choice of two wader firsts for Britain. What were they?
24. In 1988 one member of the thrush family was added to the British List and one taken away. What were they?
25. Britain's first White-crowned Black Wheatear was found in June 1982, near which Suffolk town?
26. Pallas's (Reed) Bunting was first seen in 1976. In which year was the second record?
27. Which *Dendroica* warbler made its British debut on 27 September 1981 on St Agnes?

Birds of Southern Africa

1. What is South Africa's only Critically Endangered endemic bird?
2. What species of courser does not occur in Zimbabwe at all but is found elsewhere in southern Africa?
3. Three species in Botswana are named after William Burchell. Name two.
4. If in a day's birding I saw Augur Buzzard and Kelp Gull, which country am I in?

5. Which species does the Black Widowfinch/Variable Indigobird parasitise?
6. Of the 21 species of sunbird that occur in the region 4 are endemic to Southern Africa. Name two.
7. What is the African Cuckoo's only known host species in southern Africa?
8. Why did Peter, Percy and Pamela achieve notoriety as a result of sunken 'Treasure' in July 2000?
9. What common British finch was introduced to South Africa in 1898 and continues to survive in the Cape Town area?
10. 'Tsikidzamutsetse' is the Shona name for which bird?
11. 'Hamerkop' is the Afrikaans name for which bird?
12. The Cape Vulture, a southern African endemic has become extinct as a breeding species in which southern African country?
13. All southern African honeyguides have multiple hosts except for the Slender-billed Honeyguide which only has one host. What is it?
14. Name the only southern African bird not to have a keeled sternum (breast-bone).
15. The African or Jackass Penguin has its largest single population on which island?
16. How many species of flightless bird are on the Southern African list?
17. In the southern African representatives of the family Cuculidae (Cuckoos), typically brood-parasites, only one member is polyandrous, with the male undertaking all parental care. Which one is it?
18. Which member of the Turdidae regularly takes over the nests of tunnel-nesting swallows to breed?
19. How many species of broadbill occur in Southern Africa?
20. Which American heron was observed at Velddrif, near Cape Town on 11 April 1992, the first Old World record for this species (excluding the Azores)?
21. Of birds found in Zimbabwe, name three raptors that are named after people.
22. If in a day's birding I manage to see Starred Robin, Long-tailed Shrike and Violet-backed Sunbird, which country am I in?
23. Name two species of ibis that occur in Southern Africa.
24. What species of albatross was added to the African list after being sighted on 17 May 2001 near Cape Town?
25. In the nightjars, both sexes incubate except in one species - which species is it?

26. Apart from the Pygmy Falcon, which other southern African falcon breeds regularly in cavities?
27. Which is the largest of these larks: Stark's Lark, Thick-billed Lark or Botha's Lark?
28. Out of all the species recorded in southern Africa, which has the largest wing area to weight ratio (i.e. lowest wing-loading)?
29. What is the sewage works in the Western Cape which is an Important Bird Area for Lesser Flamingo, Cape Cormorant and Hartlaub's Gull, and is threatened by construction of a new road?
30. Out of southern Africa's kingfishers, two species are facultatively co-operative - Pied Kingfisher and which other?

British Bird Songs and Calls

1. What is the speech rendition of the Yellowhammer's song?
2. What links Starling, Sedge Warbler, Red-backed Shrike and Marsh Warbler?
3. Name two species that produce a characteristic sound other than by voice.
4. Name three regular British breeding species with onomatopoeic English names .
5. What species' song sounds like a bunch of keys being rattled?
6. Who wrote *Ode to a Nightingale*?
7. Which second for Britain did Paul Dukes identify on call on St Agnes in October 1977?
8. Bill Oddie's *Little Black Bird Book* gives some sound advice as to which woodland species is making any unfamiliar calls. Which species is it?
9. Who first recognised that Willow Warbler and Chiffchaff are separate species, based on their song?
10. You are watching swallows in the summer and they all suddenly give a distinctive call, a low-pitched soft double note, variously rendered as 'soowee' or 'phoo-it'. Which species might you expect to see next?
11. "Deal o'wet, deal o'wet, deal o'wet. I do, I do, I do. Who'd do it: Pretty Dick, Pretty Dick, Pretty Dick. Who'd do it" is a rendering of which bird according to J. Lewis Bonhote in *Birds of Britain* (1907)?
12. To which bird does the following entry in Witherby's *Handbook of British Birds* refer: "Only note recorded was a low croak"?
13. To the accompaniment of which bird did Beatrice Harrison

famously play the cello in Oxted, Surrey in the 1930s?

14. Who was the German-born pioneer of British bird song recording?

15. Pairs of what rare British breeding bird produce loud penetrating duets or unison calls?

16. Name the two British breeding species with onomatopoeic specific scientific names.

17. Vaughan Williams composed a piece in praise of the song of which bird?

18. Which warbler's song has been likened to the noise of a power sewing machine?

19. Which bird's call is often described as "a titter"?

20. In which county would you be most likely to hear the song described as "a beautiful loud fluting whistle, confusable only (at a distance) with Blackbird"?

21. Prior to this year, when and where were the calls of proud parent Bee-eaters last heard in this country?

22. Which garden bird was first heard in the UK in the 1950s?

23. Name three British species that gather to lek.

24. Imitate a lekking Capercaillie.

25. Which British bird's song is featured at the beginning of Pulp's recent song *The Birds in your Garden*?

26. Only recorded here once, which American bird was singing when it was discovered in Paisley in June 1977?

27. Which British bird's song, delivered in flight, consists of several croaking noises followed by a thin sneeze-like note?

28. Which British bird is named 'Kluut' in Dutch after its distinctive call note?

29. In simple terms, how does the familiar call of a Willow Warbler differ from that of a Chiffchaff?

30. If a Great Spotted Woodpecker's call might be rendered as 'kick-kick..', how would a Lesser Spotted Woodpecker's call be similarly rendered?

Birds of Cuba

1. How many fully resident breeding species (including introductions) are found on Cuba?

2. How many species migrate to Cuba to breed?

3. Gundlach's Hawk was named after which ornithologist (give full name).

4. There are three other Cuban species that have Latin names which refer to him. Name one of these.
5. Which species nested in Cuba for the first time in 1990?
6. Which endemic species is this - *Xiphidiopicus percussus*?
7. Which species became extinct in Cuba in 1864 (or at least the last one was shot then)?
8. Which bird is known in Cuba by the local name 'Senorita del Monte'?
9. Which Bird Fair organiser found a 'rare bird' in Cuba?
10. The Cuban Sparrow isn't a sparrow at all, but a what?
11. What is the special claim to fame of the Cuban endemic species with the scientific name *Mellisuga helenae*?
12. How much does a Bee Hummingbird weigh?
13. In what year was the last confirmed sighting in Cuba of the Ivory-billed Woodpecker?
14. Which bird species is commonly called in Spanish the 'Bandera Cubana' – the Cuban flag – and why?
15. Where in Cuba would you have to go to see a Thick-billed Vireo?
16. Which three species of diurnal raptor regularly seen in Britain could you also expect to see in Cuba?
17. Which two members of the American wood-warbler family Parulidae are endemic to Cuba?
18. What do the following species have in common (apart from the fact that they all occur in Cuba and are named after the country): Cuban Parrot, Cuban Emerald, Cuban Pewee, Cuban Martin and Cuban Crow?
19. Currently, how many globally threatened species are known from Cuba?
20. When and where were the last confirmed reports of Bachman's Warbler in Cuba?
21. Which of these is the odd one out, and why: Northern Shoveler, Magnolia Warbler, Townsend's Warbler, Cape May Warbler and Greater Yellowlegs?
22. Which Cuban endemic shares its name with a card game?
23. Which Vulnerable species that breeds mainly in Canada has been recorded in the winter months on Cuba?
24. Which of these is the odd one out, and why: Spotted Rail, Zapata Rail, White-tailed Tropicbird, Yellow-headed Warbler?
25. What is the main plumage feature which distinguishes the endemic Cuban Gnatcatcher from the resident Blue-gray Gnatcatcher in winter?

GENERAL KNOWLEDGE 2002

1. How do you spell Bullfinch?
2. How do you spell Cretzschmar's Bunting?
3. What colour is the cap of a female Blackcap?
4. When was the Oriental Bird Club founded?
5. How many (Great) Bitterns visited the London Wetlands Centre on 11 January 2002?
6. In what year did the British Birdwatching Fair support Eastern Cuba?
7. What was the flagship species?
8. Which of the following have never been recorded at Rutland Water: Great Auk, Little Auk or Sparrow 'awk?
9. What is the logo of the Neotropical Bird Club
10. Barry Sheavils was sent to prison for 4 months in August 2001 in Northumberland for possessing Goshawk and Goosander eggs. What was significant about this sentence?
11. The Critically Endangered Giant Ibis is believed to be confined to 2 countries. Name one.
12. Which of the following birds does not exist? Purple-throated Sunangel, Purple-backed Sunbeam, Purple-rumped Sunreader or Purple-naped Sunbird?
13. In golf, a hole in 3 strokes under par is known as what sort of bird?
14. Which Critically Endangered Species was observed in Britain for the first time at Druridge Bay, Northumberland between May 4-7 1998?
15. How do you spell Goldfinch?
16. How do you spell Güldenstädt's Redstart?
17. What colour is the cap of a male Bullfinch?
18. When was The African Bird Club founded?
19. The population of which species in Kensington Gardens fell from 2,603 in 1925 to 4 in 2002?
20. The number of wild-caught African Grey Parrots imported into the European Union in 1999 (excluding the thousands that died in the process) was roughly 3,000, 30,000 or 300,000?
21. In what year did the British Birdwatching Fair support the Moroccan Wetlands?
22. Name one of the flagship species.
23. Whose photograph of copulating Lesser Kestrels won the Bird Photograph of the Year competition earlier this year?
24. Which of the following do you stand the best chance of seeing

near Rutland Water: Pink-headed Duck, Labrador Duck, Bombay Duck?

25. What is the logo of the Oriental Bird Club?
26. Which African species has learned to mimic the alarm call of the Meerkat when it has unearthed prey, sending it scurrying and allowing this bird a free meal?
27. Members of the Women's Royal Naval Service are known as which birds?
28. How many species of woodpecker are there on the British List?
29. There are 5 species of parrot that have bred in the wild in the UK. Name 3.
30. How do you spell Chaffinch?
31. How do you spell Phainopepla?
32. What colour is the crown of the Tree Sparrow?
33. When was the Ornithological Society of the Middle East founded?
34. What is the function of the knitted sweaters that the Tasmanian Conservation Trust have dressed Fairy Penguins in?
35. Which of the following birds does not exist? Blue-throated Starfrontlet, Blue-tufted Starthroat, Blue-breasted Starlet or Blue-eared Glossy Starling?
36. Name 2 bird species that are named after Mediterranean islands.
37. In what year did the British Birdwatching Fair support Ecuador?
38. What was the flagship species?
39. What is the logo of the African Bird Club?
40. When did Rutland Water reach top water line (full capacity) for the first time?
41. What type of pasta shares its name with a penguin?
42. What is the chief item in the diet of Verreaux's Eagle?
43. What Critically Endangered Western Palaearctic bird is being reintroduced into Austria and will be urged to migrate with the aid of a microlight?
44. What British breeding bird's song is described as churring?
45. What is the colour of the ear-like feather tufts on the Blue Eared-pheasant and the Brown Eared-pheasant?
46. How do you spell Hawfinch?
47. How do you spell Dickcissel?
48. What colour is the head of a Shoveler drake?
49. When was the Neotropical Bird Club founded?
50. Club Mediterranean is proposing to build a 260-hectare complex at Tifnit in Morocco, close to probably the last stronghold of which Critically Endangered species?

51. What is the title of the BTO's first children's book about a young Barn Swallow?
52. When was Rutland Water designated a Ramsar site?
53. Which of the following species does not exist: White-moustached Hermit, White-browed Hermit, White-whiskered Hermit or White-bearded Hermit?
54. What mammal is seriously interfering with a nest-box scheme assisting Pied Flycatchers in Okehampton?
55. What is the logo of the Ornithological Society of the Middle East?
56. How much do the first 7 volumes of the *Handbook of Birds of the World* weigh – 39lbs, 59lbs or 79lbs (18kg, 27kg or 36kg)?
57. Who wrote the slim but instructive volumes *Bird Recognition*, first published in 1947?
58. And how much did they weigh?
59. In which year did the British Birdwatching Fair support conservation in Malta?
60. And how much money did it raise (to the nearest £1000)?
61. In chess a castle is frequently referred to as which bird?
62. What is a Landrail?
63. Which British breeding bird's song is described as reeling?
64. Name two species of Indian vulture that have suffered catastrophic population declines recently.
65. Which species rears one young every 3 to 4 years on Macquarie Island, probably the lowest breeding rate of any bird?
66. How many species on the British list have the same specific name as their generic name (±2)?

BIRDFAIR 2003
Saving Madagascar's Fragile Wetlands

Madagascar has been separated from other landmasses for tens of millions of years and has evolved a unique flora and fauna. The bird life includes around 120 endemic species within 5 endemic families. Many of these endemic bird species are threatened, especially those living in Madagascar's wetlands. There is still virtually no protection of the Malagasy wetlands so the record sum of £157,000 raised at the 2003 Birdfair will be used by BirdLife International to launch the Madagascar Wetland Conservation Programme. The programme has already made exciting biological discoveries and the first real steps in conserving the wetlands by working with the local people who live by and depend on the wetlands. Fieldwork has confirmed the presence of the very rare Sakalava Rail in the wetlands of Lake Kinkony and this rarely seen species is being studied to help its conservation needs. Further studies have discovered important colonies of Madagascar Sacred Ibis and a record-breaking count of over 200 Madagascar Teal in the Mahavavy Delta. Local support for conservation is very strong, as people are aware that current regulations are being flouted, particularly hunting and over-fishing, and so an advocacy campaign is underway to contact and convince decision-makers to support local initiatives. An eco-tourism circuit based in the town of Mahajanga will start in 2004 and will demonstrate to the local people the long-term value of saving their wetlands, and raise their profile nationally and internationally.

The contestants, under the Chairmanship of Bill Oddie, were:-

Andy Mitchell (Neotropical Bird Club)
Callan Cohen (African Bird Club)
Keith Betton (Ornithological Society of the Middle East)
* Nigel Collar (Oriental Bird Club)

SPECIALIST SUBJECTS 2003
Birds of the Dominican Republic

1. How many species are endemic to the Dominican Republic?
2. Who wrote *Aves de la Republica Dominicana* ('Birds of the DR'), published by the Dominican National Museum of Natural History in 1978?
3. Which two closely related species are both known locally in the DR as 'Cuatro Ojos' ('Four-eyes')?
4. Which two members of the Procellariidae family may breed in the DR?
5. Which bird found only in Haiti and the DR is known in Haiti as the 'English Lady' (Dame Anglaise)?
6. What was the original vernacular name of White-winged Warbler, which commemorates its describer?
7. Which species did Wetmore describe as 'one of the most extraordinary members of a highly interesting extinct fauna'?
8. Which passerine is a resident on Hispaniola but principally a migrant elsewhere in the Greater Antilles?
9. Which widespread Neotropical bird is confined within the Caribbean to Hispaniola?
10. What makes *Dulus dominicus* so special?
11. Where's the white on a White-necked Crow?
12. The common name of which Hispaniolan endemic is taken from a mountain range in Haiti?
13. Which bird is known locally as the 'Perico'?
14. Which Hispaniolan endemic is a real gem?
15. As well as the endemic Hispaniolan Emerald, name two other species of hummingbird you could expect to find in the DR?
16. What is the largest bird (measured from beak to tail) regularly found in the DR?
17. What is the subspecific (or specific, if you believe Garrido *et al.*) name of the Grey-headed Quail-dove in the Dominican Republic?
18. What part of a Hispaniolan Trogon do you look at to tell if it's male or female?
19. Which bird, nowadays considered endemic to Hispaniola, was recorded in Jamaica in the 1970s?
20. Which is the most threatened bird species in Hispaniola?
21. Which introduced species lives wild in the Dominican Republic at Los Haiteses and in the Sierra de Baoruco?

22. Which famous student of pheasants watched birds in Hispaniola in 1927?
23. Which endemic species was originally described, somewhat erroneously, as an *Empidonax* flycatcher?
24. The call of which endemic species is described in the recent Helm field guide *Birds of the West Indies* as "a strong 'cua', followed by a guttural, accelerating 'u-ak-u-ak-ak-ak-ak-ak-ak-ak'"?
25. Which two species of estrildid finches have established feral populations in DR?
26. When was the first Swainson's Hawk for the West Indies discovered in the Dominican Republic (give or take one year)?
27. Which bird species is thought to be at particular risk due to the recent discovery of West Nile virus in Dominican Republic?
28. Which endemic to Hispaniola might you say looks permanently drained of colour?
29. Which one of the following duck species familiar in the UK has not been recorded in the DR: Mallard, Green-winged Teal, Northern Pintail, Northern Shoveler, Eurasian Wigeon, Gadwall?

Endemic Bird Families of Africa

1. What is so striking about mousebird eggs?
2. Gould described the Shoebill based on a specimen provided by a man who sounds like a Jane Austen novel. Who was he?
3. What is a 'Fandikalalala'?
4. Why doesn't the Speckled Mousebird occur west of the Niger River?
5. What two kinds of bird were 'mixed-up' to form the generic name of the rockfowls?
6. How many monospecific families are there in mainland Africa?
7. Only one species of guineafowl is known to use traditional roosting sites. Which one?
8. Of the six species of guineafowl, only one is found wholly in the northern hemisphere. Which one?
9. The unique feature of some members of the turaco family is the presence of two copper pigments, one red and one green. What are the names of the two pigments?
10. The family Balaenicipitidae contains only one species, the Shoebill. Spell Balaenicipitidae.
11. Which species of vanga is also found on the Comores?

12. Which endemic species is called Ombrette africaine in French?
13. Name a species that was not an African endemic 100 years ago, but is today?
14. How many days does a Shoebill chick stay in the nest after hatching?
15. Which species has the Latin name *Brachypteracias leptosomus*?
16. Where in eastern Madagascar was the White-breasted Mesite found in 1990?
17. What has the Hamerkop got on its feet in common with herons?
18. There are two explanations for the name Secretary Bird. One is that the feathers on the head look like the quill pens stuck behind the ear of a secretary. What is the other?
19. Of the 23 species of turaco, how many are found only in one country?
20. Which has the longest length - Yellow-headed or Red-headed Picathartes?
21. How many species of wattle-eye and batis are there?
22. The mousebirds, Coliidae, are split into two subfamilies, Coliinae and Urocoliinae. How many species are there in each?
23. Of the eight species of woodhoopoe, only two were described after 1900. Which two?
24. Within the turaco family, the name of the subfamily containing the typical turacos, Musophaginae, which is used now, was proposed in 1820 by Lesson, even though an earlier name was proposed by Raffinesque in 1815. What was this earlier name?
25. Which pesticide has recently been used by farmers in South Africa to eliminate sugarbirds from their protea crops?
26. What turaco has got a name in common with a gull and a goose?
27. Apart from the Hamerkop, which African species is in its own superfamily?
28. When was the first Ostrich farm set up in Cape Province (to within 5 years)?
29. Name one species in the family Raphidae.
30. Which member of an endemic African family was named after a banker?
31. The Ostrich is a member of the order known as ratites. What does 'ratite' mean?

Birds of New Zealand

1. What was the dubious claim to fame of the lighthouse keeper's cat on Stephen's Island?
2. The Wrybill is unique in having, as its name suggests, a laterally curved bill. Does it curve to the bird's a) right, b) left, or c) either way?
3. What bird, which is considered to be one of the world's rarest seabirds, was rediscovered in 1978?
4. And who rediscovered it?
5. There are five species of gull, *Larus,* listed as threatened. What's the name of the New Zealand representative?
6. Hybridisation with Pied Stilt is a significant conservation problem for the threatened Black Stilts (population 40 in 1999) – why does this occur so readily?
7. Juvenile Black Stilts are pied, and pass through various mottled plumages (almost indistinguishable from Pied/Black hybrids) before attaining the pure black plumage of adulthood. What is a foolproof way of recognising pure-bred Black Stilts in the field?
8. In 1978 a diving petrel colony previously thought to be Common Diving Petrel was identified as South Georgia Diving Petrel. Where is this colony?
9. Where and what is Toroa/Taiaroa Head, and, for a bonus, how did it get its name?
10. If you were having a 'whio', what would you be doing?
11. At one stage there was only one living female Chatham Island Robin. What was her nickname?
12. Which bird is 'Richard Henry'?
13. Which unwelcome visitor was removed from Campbell Island earlier this year?
14. What is a 'Keruru'?
15. How do you tell a Northern from a Southern Giant Petrel?
16. Which race of Tomtit has all-black plumage?
17. Which New Zealand species became extinct in 1972?
18. How many bird species previously found on the mainland of New Zealand have become extinct since 1900?
19. Which species breeds on Chatham Island - Chatham Albatross or Chatham Petrel?
20. Four species of penguin breed only in New Zealand. Name three of them.
21. What is thought to have finally caused the extinction of the Auckland Island Merganser?

22. Which weighs more - a Black-browed Albatross or a Yellow-eyed Penguin?
23. Brown Teal has been split into three species. What are the three and, apart from this, what do they have in common?
24. What colour wattles did the extinct South Island Kokako have?
25. Prior to the 2002 breeding season, when were the last Kakapo chicks hatched?
26. Where do Hutton's Shearwater breed, and at what altitude?
27. Which New Zealand honeyeater would help you with your sewing?
28. Is the black form of Pied Fantail more common on North or South Island?
29. Which endemic New Zealand family became extinct in the 20th Century?
30. The New Zealand Spotted Shag is one of the orange-footed shags in the subgenus of *Stictocarbo*. Which shag is it considered to be closely related to and where can this shag be found?

Threatened Birds of Asia

1. In which year was the last confirmed record of Crested Shelduck, (give or take 2 years)?
2. Which threatened species, whose breeding grounds are

unknown, was known to local birdcatchers as the 'Swollen-eyed bird'?

3. Name three of the four countries which host breeding colonies of Relict Gull.
4. Which Indonesian species is difficult to detect as a result of the presence of an almost identical mimic species?
5. Name the species that breeds in SW China and which is known during the non-breeding season from just a single record in peninsular Malaysia?
6. Name the species which has an estimated population in the region of 300 individuals and occupies one of the smallest natural ranges of any bird species (of 7 square kilometres)?
7. In which country lie the wintering grounds of Streaked Reed-Warbler?
8. To which island is Black-chinned Monarch endemic?
9. Green-faced Parrotfinch is a forest bird whose distribution is closely associated with what phenomenon?
10. How did Isabela Oriole, known only from Luzon in the Philippines, get its name?
11. Which 2 threatened parrotbills are endemic to China?
12. Which bird was only discovered in 1981, despite being endemic to one of the world's most economically advanced countries?
13. There are three species of the pheasant family known as tragopans classed as vulnerable, Western, Blyth's and Cabot's. What is the meaning and derivation of the word 'tragopan'?
14. Which member of the dove family is known only from a single specimen? And what sex is the specimen (for a bonus)?
15. White-eared Night Heron from China is extremely rare. There is one record from which other country?
16. There are six threatened species of Laughingthrush, *Garrulax*. Which two are endemic to China?
17. How many globally-threatened Asian hornbills are there?
18. Can you name four?
19. Using weight as the sole criterion, two species tie for the largest raptor in the world (excluding vultures). One is the Harpy Eagle, which is the other?
20. Bulwer's, Reeve's, Salvadori's, Hume's and Elliot's Pheasants are all threatened, but one is the odd one out. Why?
21. Name two of the four threatened members of the suite of 16 species that are restricted to the Western Ghats Endemic Bird Area.
22. Name the other two.

23. Which Philippine endemic shares part of its scientific name with another threatened species with a recently discovered population in Myanmar?
24. How many pittas are threatened in Asia?
25. To which island is Rufous-throated White-eye endemic?
26. How many threatened bird species are restricted to Izu Islands Endemic Bird Area? And name them for a bonus.
27. There are four hawks of the genus *Accipiter* listed in *Threatened Birds of the World* as vulnerable or endangered. Name two of the three Asian species.
28. Which SE Asian species, with a population estimated at 250 individuals in 1997 and recently found again in Vietnam, is declining as a result of hunting, disturbance and lowland deforestation?
29. Which is the sole threatened bird species only known from the lowland forests of Sumatra?
30. In taxonomic order, the first two species in *Threatened Birds of the World* are Asian, (defining Asia in its broadest sense i.e. including Irian Jaya). What are they?
31. Which species is predicted to undergo a decline of more than 80% over the next 30 years as a result of the introduction of a species of ant?

GENERAL KNOWLEDGE 2003

1. What colour are the legs of an adult Redshank?
2. What species does the kingfisher on the label of Kingfisher beer most closely resemble?
3. Will Malta's membership of the European Union provide any protection for migrant birds from its 15,000 licensed hunters?
4. An individual of which species was first ringed (as an adult) on Bardsey in May 1957 and was retrapped on 24 April 2003 (for the fourth time) making it at least 50 years old?
5. A small eastern population of Northern Bald Ibis was discovered breeding in which country in 2002?
6. Why are Teal, Osprey, Lapwing and Goldeneye always present at Rutland Water?
7. Name one of the two Endangered (or Critically Endangered) Madagascar rails?
8. Which of the following does not exist? Blackish Antbird, Black Antbird, Jet Antbird or Blackest Antbird?
9. The crissum is the area round the cloaca and undertail-coverts derived from the Latin verb 'crissare'. What does 'crissare' mean?
10. The Common Cuckoo does not regularly parasitise two of the following species: Dunnock, House Sparrow, Meadow Pipit, Northern Wheatear, Pied Wagtail and Wren. Name one.
11. Name the other.
12. Which African dove says "naMAAAqua" in anglophone Africa, according to the African Bird Club?
13. And what does it say in francophone Africa?
14. A tiger-shark in Eilat was recently found with a ram's skeleton and two sealed jars of mayonnaise in its stomach. What bird was also found in its stomach?
15. How many British species were on the Amber List indicating 'medium conservation concern' in the 2002 review?
16. What recent colonist of Cyprus is believed to be responsible for the decline of the endemic Cyprus Warbler in some parts of Cyprus?
17. The Nuthatch *Sitta europaea* now bears what descriptive adjective?
18. Name one of the Critically Endangered species on Christmas Island threatened by deforestation for a satellite launching facility and an immigration processing centre.
19. What colour are the legs of an adult Yellow-legged Gull?

20. What endearing but uncuddly introduced insectivore has been causing havoc among ground-nesting waders in the Outer Hebrides?
21. For what purpose are Hornbill tail-feathers from captive birds in zoos collected and sent to Sarawak?
22. The common name for *Turdoides altirostris* might also be applied to Comical Ali (the ex-Minister for Information in Iraq). What is it?
23. What duck won the 1952 Grand National at 100 to 7?
24. Which of the following does not exist? Beautiful Hummingbird, Marvellous Hummingbird, Stonking Hummingbird or Magnificent Hummingbird?
25. Apart from eggs, what does the male Egyptian Vulture eat to enhance its yellow iris to attract females?
26. What bird is depicted in the winning Bird Photograph of the Year this year?
27. And who was the prize-winning photographer?

28. What is the main threat to the largest British heronry (at Northward Hill RSPB reserve)?
29. Which African dove says "BLACK-a-BILL......BLACK-a-BILL" according to the African Bird Club?
30. What does it say in francophone Africa?
31. Which Brazilian endemic was last seen in the wild on 5 October 2000?
32. What adjective now describes Gannet, Pintail, Goshawk and Lapwing?
33. Which parrot was recently rediscovered in Colombia, not having been seen with certainty since 1911?
34. Masked Booby, Brown Booby and White-tailed Tropicbird have all recently returned to breed on Ascension Island again. What made this possible?
35. What colour are the legs of an adult Red-legged Partridge?
36. What is a female swan called?
37. Where do the majority of Blackcaps that winter in the UK breed?
38. What duck broke the record for the fastest steam train in 1938 at 126 mph?
39. Which of the following protected areas will be violated if a new airport is built at Cliffe in Kent: i) Special Protection Area (SPA), ii) Ramsar Site, iii) Site of Special Scientific Interest (SSSI)?
40. How does the Bay-winged cowbird differ from the other five species of cowbird in its breeding habits?
41. Name one of the two distinguished British ornithologists who both died in April this year with a combined age of 196 years and who, with others, were responsible for creating the WWF?
42. Name the other.
43. Which of the following does not exist? Needle-billed Hermit, Sword-billed Hermit, Saw-billed Hermit or Hook-billed Hermit?
44. Against what species of bird did Lesley McKighan carry out a personal vendetta in her Scottish garden, as broadcast by the BBC on 1 April 2003?
45. Which African dove says "I mou-ou-ou-ourn" in anglophone Africa according to the African Bird Club?
46. What does it say in francophone Africa?
47. How many species of vulture breed in the Massif Central in France?
48. What practically impenetrable part of the Korean peninsula was recently found to have breeding Black-faced Spoonbills and wintering White-naped and Red-crowned Cranes in it?
49. *Acrocephalus griseldi*'s home town was in the news recently. What is it?

50. The Bald Parrot (*Pionopsitta aurantiocephala*) has only recently been described, because it was previously thought to be an immature of what species?
51. What colour are the legs of an adult Greenshank?
52. If Hugh and Major Ruttledge returned to Strangford Lough, what happened to Kerry?
53. Prior to 2002 when did Red-billed Choughs last breed successfully in Cornwall (give or take five years)?
54. In what duck in Jamaica did Ian Fleming write most of the James Bond novels?
55. What event resulted in the first mainland Spanish record of White-faced Storm Petrel and the third Brown Booby for Spain in the winter 2002/2003?
56. What sex is a Reeve?
57. What is the connection between the late lamented Chris Mead and two owls, a hen, four larks and a wren?
58. Madagascar has two Critically Endangered eagles. Name one.
59. Name the other.
60. What does the Common Chiffchaff's specific name '*collybita*' mean?
61. Which African dove says "J'AI UN col-lier-er-er" in francophone Africa according to the African Bird Club?
62. And what does it say in anglophone Africa?
63. Which vitamin are Red-vented Bulbuls unable to synthesise – an inability that they share with humans, guinea-pigs, Rainbow Trout and Coho Salmon?
64. Which of the following does not exist? Kangaroo Parrot, Zebra Finch, Buffalo Weaver or Rhinoceros Hornbill?
65. The frigatebird found on Tiree in 1953 was thought to be a Magnificent Frigatebird. What species was it found to be on recent re-examination?
66. How many British species were there on the Red List indicating 'high conservation concern' in the 2002 review (10% either way)?

THE ANSWERS

ANSWERS 1992: SPECIALIST SUBJECTS
Endangered Bird Species

1. Red Kite, White-tailed Eagle and Corncrake. [This was the situation in 1992. Corncrake is still rated as Vulnerable, but White-tailed Eagle is only Near Threatened and Red Kite is another story.]
2. It was found injured and kept in a bath. [This was the last sighting of a Madagascar Pochard.]
3. 7 Black-necked, Hooded, Red-crowned, Whooping, White-naped, Siberian and Wattled. [Sadly the score is now 9 (1 Critically Endangered - Siberian, 2 Endangered - Whooping and Red-crowned, and 6 Vulnerable - Sarus, White-naped, Blue, Wattled, Hooded and Black-necked.)]
4. They all have nesting colonies of Dalmatian Pelicans.
5. 122 in 1992. [In 2000 there were 114 Threatened species (all categories) and 74 Near Threatened species.]
6. New Caledonia. ["An egg" is not an acceptable alternative answer.]
7. Interbreeding with the Pied Stilt.
8. 33 (28-38).
9. Short-tailed (or Steller's) Albatross.
10. Jack Pine Warbler.
11. Christmas Island.
12. Takahe *Notornis mantelli*.
13. Red-necked Parrot (Amazon).
14. Prince Ruspoli's Turaco.
15. Black-eared Miner.
16. Jerdon's Courser.
17. White-eyed River Martin. [There was an unconfirmed report in 1986.]
18. Brazil, Paraguay, Argentina and Uruguay.
19. Zigzag Heron.
20. Red-cockaded Woodpecker.
21. Great Bustard. [Probably less than 65% now, i.e. 45-60%.]
22. Martha.
23. Carolina Parakeet, (named 'Incas').
24. Blue or Tahitian Lory or Blue Lorikeet. [Currently classified as Vulnerable.]
25. An American millionaire wanted to set up home there.
26. Freira or Zino's Petrel.
27. The Fon.
28. The lighthouse-keeper's cat.
29. The Moas.
30. Spix's Macaw. [This biord has since disappeared and the wild population is now extinct.]
31. Goffin's Cockatoo or Tanimbar Cockatoo. [Now Near Threatened.]
32. It is nocturnal.
33. It was believed to be a witch.
34. 1962. There have been no others since. Following the recommendations of the BOU Records Committee in 2002, Houbara Bustard has been split into Houbara Bustard *Chlamydotis undulata* and Macqueen's Bustard *C. macqueenii*. The four 19th century

records were identified as *macqueenii* and, following a lengthy deliberation, so was the 1962 record. So the correct answer now is "Never".]

35. They fly away from breeding areas and cannot return as they become flightless as adults.
36. Inaccessible Island (and the bird is inaccessible Island Rail).
37. Hybridisation with Ruddy Ducks.
38. The bill shape of the male and female was dramatically different.
39. One. [The population had recovered to 259 in 1999.]
40. Pulitzer. (Pulitzer's Longbill).
41. Little Spotted was the answer in 1992. [There are now considered to be four species and all are Threatened.]
42. Great Bustard, Little Bustard and Lesser Kestrel in 1992. [Little Bustard is now classified as Near Threatened. Spanish Imperial Eagle might conveniently replace it.]

Wildfowl of the World

1. Eyton's Whistling Duck or Grass Whistling Duck. [Or Eyton's Tree Duck or Plumed Tree Duck or Red-legged Tree Duck…]
2. Coots and Rosybills. [It is parasitic.]
3. Baikal Teal.
4. Red-crested Pochard.
5. Philippa Scott, at Slimbridge on 12th March 1955.
6. Canada Goose.
7. They lack feather tracts, so feathers grow randomly over their bodies.
8. The Musk Duck.
9. Four.
10. Magpie Goose.
11. Coscoroba Swan.
12. Ross's Goose.
13. Salvadori's Duck.
14. Freckled Duck.
15. Red-crested Pochard.
16. White-headed (or Chubut) Flightless Steamer Duck.
17. Meller's Duck.
18. 1947. [However, the influx in 1994, and some other years, is widely thought to have been composed, at least partly, of wild birds.]
19. British wildfowl collections. ["America" is not an acceptable answer.]
20. Donald Duck.
21. Nene or Hawaiian Goose.
22. Pink-headed Duck. [Last seen in the wild in 1949.]

Ringing and Migration

1. Skokholm, in 1933.
2. Lundy.
3. Four years old. [The record was four years, ten months and 9 days old in 2002.]
4. The Lord Chamberlain.
5. Woodlark, Skylark, Bearded Tit, Long-tailed Tit, Starling, House Sparrow, Tree Sparrow and Corn Bunting.

6. 11. [Most birds have 10.]
7. Eritrea/Ethiopia/Somalia.
8. 28. [Allow 23-33.] [By 2002 this figure was 48.]
9. It drops its outer 5 primaries simultaneously - making it almost flightless.
10. Pied Flycatcher and Wood Warbler.
11. 12.
12. They bore biblical quotations instead of serial numbers.
13. The inside diameter of the ring is reduced with soft plasticine or florists' wax.
14. Rossitten (Baltic).
15. Hatched during the previous calendar year.
16. 1963 (1962-1964).
17. vv [two lower case 'v's.]
18. Lesser Whitethroat.
19. Canada.
20. Brazil [121 up to 1989. 167 is the latest score.]
21. Finnmark, North Norway (mainly Tana Estuary).
22. Zugunruhe.
23. Slender-billed Curlew.
24. Arctic Tern.
25. Its size. [So far.]
26. Corncrake and Aquatic Warbler.
27. Red-necked Stint.

Ornithological Literature

1. David Lack.
2. Lundy and Noss.
3. Witherby, Jourdain, Ticehurst and Tucker.
4. Sir Julian Huxley.
5. Janet Kear. [In 1992, but Dr Mark O'Connell in 2002.]
6. J. G. Keulmans.
7. 1953 [1952-1954.]
8. Thomas Pennant and the Hon. Daines Barrington.
9. Malimbus.
10. Swift.
11. Guy Mountfort.
12. Gannet.
13. Arthur Cleveland Bent.
14. Howard Saunders.
15. Thomas Bewick.
16. Pheasants (Phasianidae).
17. Eric Ennion.
18. William Henry Hudson.
19. Birds of Paradise (Paradisaeidae).
20. The Auk.
21. *Pheasant Jungles*.
22. Pica Press. [This is now part of Christopher Helm Publishers and owned by A & C Black.]
23. Josep del Hoyo.
24. Peter Harrison.
25. Audubon's *Birds of America* (1st edition).

GENERAL KNOWLEDGE 1992

1. Great Crested Grebe.
2. A Swallow.
3. It holds a stick in its bill to winkle insects from holes.
4. Skylark. [In the New Atlas covering 1988-91, the Wren had the honour.]
5. 3,875. [3,862 was given as the answer in 1992, which was slightly erroneous. In the first Atlas, Fair Isle and each Channel Island were treated as one 10-km square each, i.e. 6 squares instead of the18 that they now contain. In the New Atlas they were treated in the same way as the rest of the British Isles. So 3,863 would have been correct in 1992.]
6. From the Greek 'Tetra', the combining form of 'Tettares/Tessares' meaning 'Four'. (A tetrad is an area of 4 square kilometres).
7. The Louse-fly or Flat-fly.
8. The BTO's Birds of Estuaries Enquiry.
9. Hampshire. [This was in fact an incorrect question, because the first record of a Cetti's Warbler in Britain (post-Hastings Rarities) was at Titchfield Haven, Hampshire on 4th March 1961.]
10. 1947.
11. Left.
12. Ivory Gull.
13. Balranald.
14. 54. [In 2003 there were 156.]
15. A hummingbird [endemic to the Andes.]
16. 25,000 [25,216 feathers were counted on a Whistling Swan by an underemployed ptilomaniac.]
17. Scottish Crossbill.
18. Because it is extinct. [Probably. It is the Pink-headed Duck, but it may conceivably hang on in Myanmar.]
19. Hedge Accentor. [The Dunnock has had a reprieve in *British Birds* as the name Hedge Accentor "has been almost completely shunned".]
20. Willow Warbler.
21. Kestrel.
22. Accentors (Prunellidae).
23. Emperor Penguin.
24. Many males mated with many females.
25. Kingfisher, because it does not have helpers at the nest.
26. The release of captive-bred birds will need to be licensed.
27. 400 pairs. [350-450 allowed]
28. European Sparrowhawk.
29. Merseyside.
30. Size. (Barn Owl's are bigger).
31. To wait for them to open.
32. Fiji.
33. Borneo.
34. Fair Isle.
35. Farne Islands.
36. Allen's Gallinule [although a second moribund bird was found 100 years later at Portland on 10th Feb 2002.]
37. Gamebirds (pheasants, partridges, grouse etc). [Young auks do not really fly,

although they make a good fist of trying.]
38. Twite.
39. European Bee-eater. [This question was set in 1992 before the most recent breeding occurrence in 2002.]
40. Mist nets.
41. Turtle Dove.
42. Rook.
43. Bird photography.
44. Moustached Warbler.
45. Hornbills.
46. The first *Archaeopteryx* fossil remains.
47. Wren.
48. Greenland White-fronted Goose.
49. Crested Tit.
50. Floating on the sea.
51. Lake Neusiedl/Neusiedlersee
52. Skuas.
53. Twelve. Cetti's Warbler is the exception with ten.
54. Sacred Ibis.
55. Magellan Flightless Steamer Duck. [This was the official answer, but it would be interesting to know whether the Falkland Island Flightless Steamer Duck or the White-headed Flightless Steamer Duck are not as fast.]
56. Common Poorwill.
57. Golden Whistler *Pachycephala pectoralis* (73!). [Allowing for taxonomic dispute, this answer was probably about right in 1992, although not any longer. According to Howard and Moore (3rd edition), Golden Whistler only has 7 subspecies now, its 66 ex-co-subspecies being included among other (new) species, such as Fulvous-tinted, Black-chinned and Banda Sea Whistlers. Island Thrush holds the record currently with 51 subspecies]
58. Fairy Tern. [Also known as White Tern]
59. Bald Eagle. [Arguably, megapodes probably build bigger nests. Australian Brush-turkey nests on Kangaroo Island averaged 6.8 tonnes, and Orange-footed Scrubfowl mounds have been variously measured as 8 metres high, 51 metres circumference, >100 cubic metres volume and 50 tonnes weight.]
60. Maleo. [This was the answer in 1992. The Moluccan Megapode is also classified as Vulnerable and buries its eggs in the sand, and Bruijn's Brush-turkey and Biak Megapode, both Vulnerable Indonesian species, may also bury their eggs, but not enough is known.]
61. Arctic Tern.
62. Roadrunner.
63. Marsh Warbler.
64. Sword-billed Hummingbird.
65. Charles G. Sibley & Burt L. Monroe, Jr.
66. Three in 1992. [Corncrake, White-tailed Eagle and Scottish Crossbill. In 2004, it is One: Corncrake is still Vulnerable, but White-tailed Eagle has now eased to Near Threatened and Scottish Crossbill is Data Deficient.]

ANSWERS 1993: SPECIALIST SUBJECTS
Migration

1. False. [It may be unlikely, but it is certainly a migrant.]
2. Bar-tailed Godwit. [There is now a fourth: a huge gathering of 2.4–2.8 million Oriental Pratincoles was observed in 2004, smashing the previous estimate of its world population by many times.]
3. Bonn.
4. None. [Since then two Agreements on birds have been signed and there have been four Memoranda of Understanding concerning birds.]
5. South-west. [West is also allowable.]
6. Jean Dorst.
7. Abmigration.
8. Zugunruhe – a German word for migratory restlessness.
9. 50%. [Accept 45-55%.]
10. Camlica Hills [pronounced 'Chamlicha'.]
11. Ruby-throated Hummingbird.
12. Norway.
13. Normally only one, in northern South America.
14. 12.5. [Accept 12 or 13.]
15. A pass in the French Pyrenees.
16. Madagascar.
17. Greenland and Eastern Canada.
18. Nowhere – it's flightless.
19. The Wadden Sea [same as British birds.]
20. Sand Martin and Sedge Warbler.

The Dartford Warbler

1. 11 pairs.
2. Marmora's Warbler.
3. Wavy/with wave-like markings.
4. Colour of the mantle and scapulars.
5. 90p in 1993. [£1.00 now.]
6. Spain.
7. Hampshire.
8. In the logo of The Hampshire and Isle of Wight Naturalists' Trust.
9. 2 – Morocco and Algeria. [It is a winter visitor to Tunisia and a vagrant to Libya.]
10. Ireland.
11. Habitat loss – destruction, degradation and fragmentation.
12. Bexleyheath.
13. 1773. [Shot in 1773, but described in 1787.]
14. 1983 (18th May) at St Abb's Head. [Accept 1978-1988.]
15. Red-eye.
16. Blackberry (Bramble).
17. 4.
18. Sardinia.

19. Primaries six and seven are the longest.
20. *undata* – 12.8mm, compared with 12.5mm.

Geese of the World

1. Lesser White-fronted Goose *Anser erythropus* from the Greek *eruthros* (red) and *pous* (foot).
2. The race Cackling Goose *minima*. Population c. 150,000.
3. Every 3 minutes [from Owen, M. 1971 in *The Journal of Applied Ecology* 8: 905-917, who investigated wild birds feeding at Slimbridge.]
4. Nene or Hawaiian Goose. [Well, not actually. Canada Goose breeds in the wild in New Zealand (*vide infra*).]
5. 600%. [It is not very clear what this question means and what is meant by Siberian Bean Goose. For the record, the combined population of *Anser fabalis rossicus*, *A. f. middendorffii* and *A. f. serrirostris* was 155,000-195,000 in 2002.]
6. It is much whiter.
7. No, four other species have occurred there – White-fronted, Emperor, Canada and Brant [Brent Goose.]
8. 5,000m.
9. Red-breasted and Lesser White-fronted Geese.
10. Cape Barren Goose.
11. Cackling Goose *Branta canadensis minima*.
12. They have reduced webbing between the toes.
13. Ruddy-headed Goose.
14. Bar-headed Goose.
15. White-fronted, Red-breasted and Greylag. [Although not in the original answer, Egyptian Goose also was depicted in ancient Egyptian paintings. It was the sacred bird of the god Geb, the god of land.]
16. After the Sandwich Islands, alias the Hawaiian Islands [but they also eat sandwiches!]
17. Canada Goose.
18. Pink-footed Goose.
19. Egyptian Goose.
20. They can all stick their bills up their . . . . . .!

Starlings of the World

1. Oxpeckers (Red-billed and Yellow-billed).
2. Woodpecker Starling/Grosbeak Starling/Finch-billed Myna *Scissirostrum dubium*.
3. Orioles, Icteridae. [Military Starling is/was also a local Falkland Island name for the Long-tailed Meadowlark *Sturnella loyca*, which had a number of other synonyms, such as Red-breasted Starling and Robin.]
4. *Aplonis*.
5. Glossy Starlings.
6. Bali Starling/Bali Myna/Rothschild's Myna.
7. Because they ate locusts.
8. One – Metallic or Shining Starling.
9. Two – *zetlandicus* on Shetland and *vulgaris* elsewhere.
10. *Aplonis* (22 spp), followed by *Sturnus* and *Lamprotornis* (16 spp each). [The

taxonomists have been busy since and there is no consensus, as far as we can make out. Current scores seem to be *Aplonis* (19-22 or 24 with extinct species), *Lamprotornis* (20-23) and *Sturnus* (15-16).]

11. Wattled Starling. [In the breeding season the head feathers are lost and it grows wattles. These are resorbed in the non-breeding season and the feathers are grown again.]
12. Daurian Starling. [Since 1993 there was a second record in 1997, but it was placed in Category D.]
13. Copper-tailed Glossy Starling and Abbott's Starling.
14. Increasing (in 1993). [Sadly this is no longer the case.]
15. Slender-billed Chestnut-winged Starling.
16. 7 (in 1993). [Depressingly the score is now 9. There are 2 Critically Endangered (Pohnpei Mountain Starling and Bali Myna), 2 Endangered (White-eyed Starling and Black-winged Starling) and 5 Vulnerable (Santo Mountain Starling, Rarotonga Starling, Atoll Starling, Abbott's Starling and White-faced Starling), plus another 8 Near Threatened (Rusty-winged Starling, Tanimbar Starling, Yellow-eyed Starling, Copper-tailed Glossy-starling, Helmeted Myna, Apo Myna, Bare-eyed Myna and Sri Lanka Myna).]
17. False. Resident in Iceland but summer visitor to Lapland.
18. False. Common Starling occurs there in winter.

GENERAL KNOWLEDGE 1993

1. Black.
2. Dr Chris Feare.
3. Resplendent Quetzal.
4. Orkneys.
5. Flowerpeckers.
6. Magpie-Lark of Australia – which builds its nest from mud.
7. Crab Plover – which nests in the dark, down a sandy burrow.
8. Fair Isle, where most Pallas's Grasshopper Warblers have been seen in Britain.
9. Blakiston's Fish Owl.
10. House Sparrow.
11. Cassowaries. [Their sharp central claws have claimed human lives.]
12. Kakapo. [A bird with a population of fewer than 100 individuals can hardly be said to be 'commonly exhibiting' anything!]
13. Echolocation.
14. They all produce 'crop-milk' – a secretion of the oesophagus with which they feed their young after hatching.
15. Gannet *Sula bassana* from Sula Sgeir and Bass Rock. [The generic name is no longer *Sula* but *Morus*.]
16. Feathers.
17. Red. [This is only true for the male. The female's is brown with a reddish tint in summer.]
18. Eric Simms.
19. Black Swan.
20. Swan (of Avon).
21. Norfolk coast.
22. In Ethiopia. [The Abyssinian Catbird is endemic to Ethiopia and unrelated to the

Australian or American Catbirds.]

23. Turacos.
24. Pechora Pipit, Terek Sandpiper, Amur Falcon (and the mythical Ob Skua.)
25. False. A number of species do migrate, e.g. the Australian Swift Parrot.
26. Purple Finch.
27. Hispaniola. (Dominican Republic and Haiti).
28. False. Its favourite food is figs. [It is named for its looks, not its habits.]
29. 230.
30. None. [Incidentally, there is no consistency in this quiz. Old and new nomenclature are used more or less randomly – a bit like metric units.]
31. The rest of the world.
32. Toucans. (Ramphastidae).
33. Kestrel.
34. White.
35. Norman Elkins.
36. Isles of Scilly.
37. Vent or undertail-coverts.
38. Little Owl *Athene noctua*.
39. Pheasant.
40. Franklin's Gull.
41. Azure-winged Magpie.
42. True. It's a small rail in the genus *Sarothrura*. There are 9 species, all in Africa or Madagascar.
43. 160 (held by Bill Oddie and team). [The record is now 162 set by the 'Norfolk Nomads' on 14 May 2000.]
44. Little Auk.
45. Frigate birds.
46. ca. 140 million years ago. [Accept 20 either way – millions, that is.]
47. Thrush Nightingale [derived from the German name for this species.]
48. It can go either way.
49. South America – c. 3,100 species.
50. Redwing.
51. Malcolm Ogilvie.
52. Hawaiian Goose or Nene.
53. Black. [But only in the case of the Black-legged Kittiwake. Astoundingly, the Red-legged Kittiwake has legs of an entirely different colour.]
54. Cetti's Warbler.
55. Redshank – in the far north-west.
56. Phainopepla is not named for its call.
57. Oilbird.
58. Budgerigar (or Budgie).
59. Whooping and Sandhill Cranes.
60. Dark, not white, rump.
61. Arctic Loon.
62. True. It is common in Alaska.
63. It is a taxonomic order for listing bird families. It was originally adopted by Ernst Mayr and followed by Peters and by Howard and Moore.
64. Hummingbird.
65. 1662, when on offshore islands. [The previously recognised last record in 1681 is now believed to have been a sighting of Red Rails.]
66. 90 species.

ANSWERS 1994: SPECIALIST SUBJECTS
Crows of the Genus Corvus

1. Long-billed Crow.
2. *zugmayeri*. [from Pakistan.]
3. Pied Crow.
4. The Kona District (the western slopes of the island). [Population – 3.]
5. *Corvus orru*.
6. Australia. [The Little Raven was split from the Australian Raven.]
7. At 10-15 months.
8. 1 to 1.5 kg. (2-3 lbs).
9. South America.
10. Hard ground makes foraging difficult.
11. Rook.
12. White irides (eyes).
13. Cuba and Hispaniola.
14. By dropping them from the air onto a hard surface.
15. "Nevermore".
16. Two. [This was the 1994 answer. The current score is seven with two in the Netherlands and one in each of Russia, Finland, Sweden, Denmark and France.]
17. Twelve years.
18. a) Three and b) four. [This was the official answer in 1994. The question seems somewhat ambiguous. Does it imply that there is/was unanimity among taxonomists, who recognised three races in Europe and four races in Asia and North America? Or does it mean that European taxonomists recognise three races, but Asian and North American recognise four? My reference books describe 4-6 races in Europe, 4 races in Asia, 2-3 races in North America and 1 race in Africa.]
19. Jackdaw has four tertials, the others have five.
20. Banggai Crow *Corvus unicolor*, Flores Crow *C. florensis*, Marianas Crow *C. kubaryi* and Hawaiian Crow *C. hawaiiensis*. [Hawaiian Crow is now Critical, Banggai, Flores and Mariana remain Endangered. Cuban Palm Crow *C. minutus* is also now Endangered and White-necked Crow *C. leucognaphalus* is Vulnerable. In addition, Brown-headed Crow *C. fuscicapillus* and Hispaniolan Palm Crow *C. palmarum* are now considered Near Threatened.]

RSPB Reserves

1. Llyn Penrhyn, Llyn Dinam and Treflesg. [To confuse the issue, there are two small lakes (Llyn Carnau and Llyn Cerrig Bach) in the Valley Lakes/Wetlands with which the RSPB is not involved, but the RSPB does own Llyn Traffwll, but this is not part of the Valley Lakes/Wetlands. Clear?]
2. Blacktoft Sands.
3. 88%. [Allow 83-93%.] [It is now 74% of the British list with 680 species.]
4. 29. [Allow 26-32.] [Now 44 species.]
5. Leighton Moss.

6. Dungeness.
7. Pied Flycatcher.
8. Knot.
9. Dartford (Warbler).
10. Because drainage of surrounding land was believed to have affected its ornithological interest.
11. Almost 10,000 acres. [Allow 9,500 to 10,500.]
12. Red-necked Phalarope.
13. Broadleaved woodland (mainly oak).
14. Dungeness.
15. 1931. [Allow 1926 to 1936.]
16. Minsmere.
17. Hodbarrow.
18. Berney Marshes.
19. One pound.
20. 1948.

The Ruddy Duck

1. Schwarzkopf-Ruderente.
2. Jamaica.
3. *andina* or *ferruginea*.
4. *Oxyura jamaicensis ferruginea*.
5. Towards the male. (There are usually more males than females).
6. Black in autumn/winter to blue in spring/summer.
7. Bull-necked Teal.
8. *Anas*.
9. Panama.
10. The Netherlands.
11. Gmelin.
12. 'Bubblebreast'.
13. True.
14. Seven.
15. (Dark) grey.
16. About 1.25 lbs. [Allow 1-1.5 lbs, or 500-800 gms.]
17. 40-50 days.
18. Southern South America. [Southern Colombia to Tierra del Fuego.]
19. 8-10.
20. It plummeted because hunters found that they tasted good.

Birds of Indonesia

1. Halmahera.
2. Rufous Woodcock (also known as Horsfield's, Indonesian and Dusky Woodcock *Scolopax saturata*).
3. Three from: Milky Stork, Woolly-necked Stork, Storm's Stork and Lesser Adjutant.
4. Borneo.
5. One. [Sombre Kingfisher *Todiramphus funebris*, although the Blue-and-white Kingfisher *Todiramphus diops* occurs on only a few other islands.]

6. It is the Invisible Rail.
7. Satanic Eared-Nightjar *Eurostopodus diabolicus*. [Although it has been seen since this question was originally set in 1994 - in Lore Lindu National Park in a number of areas and possibly elsewhere.]
8. Bay Owl.
9. Kukila.
10. None.
11. Far Eastern Curlew.
12. Minivets *Pericrocotus*.
13. Australian (not Spot-billed).
14. 5-7 grams.
15. Blue and black. (Asian Fairy-Bluebird).
16. Cerulean Paradise Flycatcher/Sangihe Blue Flycatcher. [This was true when this question was set in 1994 - but happily it was rediscovered in 1998 and subsequently 21 individuals were located. So it's not all bad news.]
17. Satanic Eared-Nightjar.
18. Black-chinned Monarch.
19. Rueck's Blue Flycatcher.
20. Slaty-backed Thrush and Fawn-breasted Thrush.

GENERAL KNOWLEDGE 1994

1. Snipe.
2. Sleepy Cisticola. [It doesn't exist.]
3. Red.
4. South and Central America (as far north as Texas).
5. A wader.
6. Six.
7. Bonxie. [There may well be others, but it depends on how "often-used" is interpreted.]
8. The observatory building on Bardsey.
9. White Bishop, unless referring to chess, in which case Red Bishop is the odd one out.
10. Blue Crane.
11. Red-throated Diver.
12. Wryneck. [most recently in 1904. Breeding by the other two has been strongly suspected, but never proved.]
13. Professor Alfred Newton.
14. Ninety. [He died in 2003 aged 98.]
15. Pheasant.
16. Larks.
17. Laughing Cisticola. [It doesn't exist].
18. Yellow.
19. Africa.
20. A parrot.
21. Zygodactyl.
22. Central or South America.
23. Eric Ennion.
24. *Glareola maldivarum* (Oriental Pratincole).

25. Skokholm.
26. Blackpoll Warbler, in 1968 and 1976, both on Bardsey.
27. Cranes.
28. (Black-backed) Forktail.
29. Wren
30. 9,800,000.
31. Cushman Murphy – one a reviewer, one an ornithologist.
32. Clint Eastwood.
33. Starling.
34. Black-winged Cisticola. [It doesn't exist].
35. Red.
36. Australasia.
37. A roller.
38. The Americas. [There is a small feral population of Red-whiskered Bulbuls in Miami and Los Angeles.]
39. Great Auk.
40. John Busby.
41. *Phylloscopus armandii* Yellow-streaked Warbler. [The other two being Dusky and Radde's. In fact, *P. armandii* has never been recorded in the UK.]
42. Cream/pale brown (with dark brown culmen and cutting edge at the tip).
43. Harrier.
44. Hobby.
45. Swans; there were 59.
46. Dent Island. [A population was recently released onto Codfish Island and are apparently established now.]
47. Sir Landsborough Thomson. [Note that this was the *New Dictionary of Birds*, not to be confused with the newer *A Dictionary of Birds* (1985) edited by Bruce Campbell and Elizabeth Lack, nor with the older *Dictionary of Birds* (1896) edited by Alfred Newton.]
48. Gilbert White.
49. Polish bird society. [Ogólnopolskie Towarzystwo Ochrony Ptakow.]
50. Goldfinches.
51. Tree-perching Cisticola. [It doesn't exist].
52. Black. [If one were politically correct, the question would have referred specifically to the Black-billed Magpie rather than the Yellow-billed, but we think that would have made it too easy.]
53. Asia.
54. A hummingbird.
55. Treecreeper. [This is another question that has been compromised by the new nomenclature, as we should be talking about Eurasian Treecreepers now.]
56. Raspberryquit. [It doesn't exist].
57. Impeyan Pheasant.
58. Cetti's Warbler.
59. Yellow-rumped Warbler.
60. Willow Tit and Marsh Tit.
61. Pied Flycatcher and Redstart.
62. Ghana.
63. (Reg) Moreau.
64. Belgium.
65. Bruce Campbell and Elizabeth Lack.
66. New Zealand. [She was a Royal Albatross, ringed before the war, but she did not come back in 2000.].

ANSWERS 1995: SPECIALIST SUBJECTS
Sylvia Warblers

1. Four.
2. Dartford Warbler.
3. *Sylvia s. sarda* is larger, and darker (especially below).
4. Madeira.
5. Above.
6. Croatia. (After Spain).
7. Increasing. [Whether this is still so is not so certain. Following the natural colonisation of Cyprus by Sardinian Warblers, the Cyprus Warbler has declined in some areas, especially at lower altitudes.]
8. Spectacled Warbler has rufous on the wings.
9. Sardinian Warbler.
10. *Sylvia melanothorax*.
11. Sardinian Warbler. [Although this was apparently the answer in 1995, Marmora's Warbler *Sylvia sarda* is darker.]
12. Lesser Whitethroat.
13. Dartford Warbler.
14. Rüppell's Warbler and Ménétries's Warbler.
15. Dartford.
16. (North) Italy.
17. Zero.
18. Ménétries.
19. Marmora's Warbler – not Sardinian.
20. Common Whitethroat.
21. Five.
22. Two.

Threatened Wildfowl

1. Norfolk. [Stirlingshire also regularly holds wintering Taiga Bean Geese.]
2. Lough Foyle.
3. Mandarin Duck.
4. Crested Shelduck.
5. Pink-headed Duck. [Reports of its continued existence in north-east India was due to confusion with Red-crested Pochard.]
6. River pollution resulting from deforestation.
7. Nene (or Hawaiian Goose).
8. The Yangtze River basin, China.
9. Two of: Turks and Caicos, Cayman Islands and British Virgin Islands.
10. 1000. [1995 answer. Although White-headed Ducks still winter in the Caspian Sea, their numbers fluctuate greatly and data is sparse, so no accurate figure can be given.]
11. Brine flies and shrimps.
12. 75,000. [This was the 1991-95 estimate. In 1996 it was 88,000, but recent extremes of weather on the wintering grounds and poor breeding conditions on the tundra

has resulted in a noticeable reduction in population.]
13. Hawaii and Maui. [It also occurs on Kaua'i now.]
14. Lake Alaotra, Madagascar. [Although it is most probably now extinct.]
15. 1971. [Strong reservations have been expressed on the reliability of this record, which was given as the answer in 1995. 1964 is probably the last reliable sighting.]
16. Ruddy-headed Goose. [Recent population estimate was 14,000-27,000.]
17. Nowhere – it is the White-headed Flightless Steamer Duck.
18. White-winged Wood Duck *Cairina scutulata*.
19. Madagascar and Mauritius.
20. It doesn't. It weighs more.
21. Scaly-sided Merganser *Mergus squamatus*.

Birds of Morocco

1. 270 birds. [The 1994 estimate was 50-270 birds.]
2. Ruddy Duck.
3. Five.
4. Glaucous-winged Gull.
5. Pesterers [in *Follow that Bird*.]
6. CPCN (Comité des Programmes de Conservation de la Nature).
7. No. [It now does have legal protection.]
8. Merdja Zerga.
9. Alpine Chough.
10. Tunisia, Spain and France.
11. David and Jane Bannerman.
12. Audouin's Gull.
13. French or Paris.
14. Ring Ouzel.
15. Bob Spencer.
16. 1,778.
17. 76. [As at March 2004 the total had risen to 82 species involving a grand total of 2,734 birds.]
18. Dotterel.
19. Gulls.
20. Five, possibly six. [Alpine, Common, Pallid, Little and White-rumped, and possibly Plain.]
21. Levaillant's Green Woodpecker.
22. Firecrest.

British Warblers

1. *abietinus* and *tristis*.
2. Rüppell's Warbler.
3. Eric Simms.
4. Skokholm.
5. Aquatic Warbler.
6. 1968 and 1969.
7. Lesser Whitethroat.

8. 13.
9. 17,200. [1993 estimate.]
10. 1972.
11. 7. [It was 5 in 2002, which was another good year. There have only been 47 records since 1958.]
12. Sedge Warbler.
13. Willow Warbler.
14. Three. [*Acrocephalus schoenobaenus.*]
15. Two.
16. Six. [*abietinus*, *collybita*, *brevirostris*, *caucasicus*, *menzbieri* and *tristis,* but the taxonomy has since changed with some taxa being elevated to full species.]
17. Leaf watcher.
18. Willow Warbler.
19. They become increasingly frugivorous (fruit-eating).
20. Blackcap.
21. 212 species. [191-233 is acceptable.]

GENERAL KNOWLEDGE 1995

1. A grebe.
2. The Woodpecker.
3. Edward Armstrong.
4. The Raven.
5. H.F.Witherby.
6. Spain.
7. Graculus.
8. A Grasshopper Warbler.
9. Siskin.
10. Iceland.
11. Blacktoft Sands.
12. Cormorants.
13. Terek Sandpiper.
14. Double-spurred Francolin.
15. On the Isle of Man.
16. Russia.
17. Arctic Skua.
18. Little Owl.
19. John Buxton.
20. Norway.
21. Because "it lays its eggs in a paper bag". [Non-exhaustive research has revealed that various other authors have written odes on the subject of the Shag's imprudent laying habits, its anti-lightning purpose and the tidy habits of vagrant bears, among them W.H.Auden, Christopher Isherwood and, of course, Anon.]
22. A Bittern.
23. Marsh Tit.
24. The Faeroes.
25. Romney Marsh.
26. Bitterns.
27. Oldsquaw.

28. Broad-billed Sandpiper.
29. Crested Coot.
30. Spain.
31. St Kentigern.
32. Ruddy Duck.
33. Long-tailed Tit. [The editor doesn't know where these scatological terms come from. His *Dictionary of Slang* contains none of these terms, (although it does have "shite-poke" meaning Bittern), and it does contain the most lewd words you could ever dream of, as well as some I hope you would never dream of.]
34. A kingfisher.
35. R. K. Murton.
36. Geoffrey Chaucer.
37. Bulgaria.
38. A Water Rail.
39. A petrel. [*Pterodroma feae*, also known as Fea's Petrel or Cape Verde Petrel.]
40. Robin.
41. Romania.
42. 1972.
43. Needs Ore Point, Hampshire.
44. Eared Grebe.
45. Stilt Sandpiper.
46. Lundy.
47. Norway.
48. Hobby.
49. A Guillemot.
50. A nightingale.
51. Guy Mountfort.
52. Edward Thomas.
53. Willow Tit.
54. The Netherlands.
55. A handsaw.
56. A Snipe.
57. Yellow Wagtail.
58. Italy.
59. 1982.
60. Whimbrel.
61. Yellow-billed Loon.
62. Buff-breasted Sandpiper.
63. Audouin's and Yellow-legged Gulls.
64. The Farne Islands.
65. Belarus.
66. *Sandgrouse.*

ANSWERS 1996: SPECIALIST SUBJECTS
The New Atlas of Breeding Birds of Britain and Ireland

1. Bodil Enoksson.
2. 240,000. (Accept 220,000-260,000).
3. Probable or confirmed breeding in 1968-72, not recorded in 1988-91.
4. Cornwall.
5. One.
6. Humberside.
7. It is subject to brackish tides.
8. Wren.
9. 7,100,000 [7 million.]
10. Robin.
11. Wren.
12. Windsor Castle.
13. Crested Tit.
14. It is the top row of conventionally coded tetrads (EJPUZ).
15. 204 [accept 200-209.]
16. Wingfield.
17. Tawny Owl.
18. None, but I could be proved wrong.
19. Cetti's Warbler.
20. The data are identified both by basic colour and by intensity of shade.
21. Common Buzzard.
22. Wren.
23. Humphrey P. Sitters.
24. Red-throated Diver, Golden Eagle, Buzzard, Peregrine, Little Tern and Chough.
25. Wryneck. [Red-backed Shrike was a close contender - present in 111 squares in the first Atlas but only 15 in the New Atlas, compared to Wryneck's 48 squares in the first Atlas and 6 in the New Atlas.]
26. More than 99%. [Accept 98-100%.] [The New Atlas was published in 1993. In Jan 1995 Finland and Sweden joined the EC, both with populations of Golden Plover greater than Britain's, so that this answer is no longer correct; the current proportion is about 15%, the change being purely geopolitical.]
27. David Glue.
28. 275,732. [Accept 250,000-300,000.]
29. 3,858. [Accept 3,800-3,900.]
30. No-one, as there isn't one.

Swans of the World

1. 25 bones.
2. W. Yarrell (1845).
3. The name seems to have been given to these birds by London poulterers, who imported young swans for the table from Eastern Europe, where the Polish morph is much commoner than in Britain.

4. 35 days. (Accept 33-37).
5. Zeus.
6. 41 degrees (Centigrade).
7. Abbotsbury, in Dorset.
8. The Worshipful Company of Vintners and the Worshipful Company of Dyers.
9. The odd cygnet, in a brood of uneven number, left after its equal division between the owners of its two parents.
10. 25,216 feathers. (Accept 24,000-26,000). [This has been a General Knowledge question more than once. The idea of someone laboriously counting 25,216 feathers for some absurdly heroic piece of scientific research seems to appeal to quiz setters.]
11. Maud.
12. It does not carry them on its back.
13. The Chatham Swan/New Zealand Swan *Cygnus sumnerensis*.
14. 22.5kg. [Accept 20-25kg.]
15. 1876. [Accept 1870-1880.]
16. Bewick's.
17. Black-necked Swan.
18. Coscoroba.
19. Their purity.
20. Trumpeter Swan has a straight culmen; in Whistling Swans it is slightly concave.
21. 3.6 to 4kg.
22. 6.4kg. [Accept 6.2-6.6kg.]
23. Mute Swan.
24. Yellowstone Park.
25. Blue-grey.
26. They appear to be centrally parted.
27. Michael Drayton.
28. Jean Sibelius.
29. William Yarrell.

Identification of Palaearctic Waders

1. Dotterel.
2. Solitary Sandpiper. [Rendering bird song into words is somewhat personal and has its drawbacks. The first three reference books that the editor consulted for verbal rendering of Solitary Sandpiper call were: 1) 'tew' or 'pit' extended into 'tou-tou-wit' or 'peet-weet', 2) 'twik' or 'pit' extended into 'twit-twit' or 'peep-weep-weep' or 'pleet-weet-weet', and 3) 'peet' extended into 'peet-weet-weet'. So, take your pick.]
3. Long-billed Dowitcher. [In 1996 this was deemed to be the correct answer. Opinion veers toward Short-billed now with the caveat that the three races of Short-billed overlap each other as well as Long-billed in quality and quantity of tiger-stripes. So either answer is correct.]
4. It is almost pure white, whereas the Curlew's is darker and heavily flecked.
5. Greater's call is trisyllabic ('Tu-tu-tu'); Lesser's call is monosyllabic ('Tu') or disyllabic ('Tu-tu').
6. Collared Pratincole *Glareola pratincola*.
7. Upland Sandpiper.
8. No. Avocets have a wholly white tail.

9. Common Snipe. [Pintail and Swinhoe's Snipes have 20 or more.]
10. *Calidris a. arctica.*
11. Grey-tailed Tattler. [Not Amami Woodcock, which has brownish legs and strongly patterned upperparts.]
12. Little Ringed Plover. [Long-billed Plover's call rises in pitch; Ringed Plover does not normally occur there.]
13. Cream-coloured Courser. [Hudsonian Godwit and Black-winged Pratincole have white rumps, and Grey Plover isn't rare.]
14. Crab Plover, which nests in burrows.
15. Ruff.
16. Dotterel and Sociable Plover.
17. Terek Sandpiper. [Curlews, godwits, dowitchers, snipes and oystercatchers can also have the bill longer than the tarsus, but none of these has bright yellow legs.]
18. Female Far Eastern Curlew.
19. Killdeer and Three-banded Plover [seen recently in Egypt.]
20. Yellowish.
21. Killdeer.
22. Stone Curlew has a white bar above the pale wing bar; Senegal Thick-knee does not.
23. Nordmann's Greenshank has much shorter tibia.
24. Dowitcher. [This question has been altered from its previous almost impossible phrasing, which is not to say that some of the questions in this section are not also almost impossible! The name was used before the Nearctic dowitchers were split into Long-billed and Short-billed.]
25. Red-necked Stint has dark lores that run through and behind the eye, whereas Little Stint has a reduced dark area on the lores separated from the eye.
26. Kittlitz's Plover.
27. The legs of Greater Sand Plover extend beyond the tail but in Lesser Sand Plover they are hardly visible. (The white wing-bar also extends slightly closer to the body in Lesser Sand Plover.)
28. White-rumped Sandpiper.
29. Three-banded Plover.

Birds of Egypt

1. Ostrich.
2. Sudan Golden Sparrow.
3. Desert Sparrow.
4. Red-breasted Goose.
5. Thoth.
6. White-breasted Kingfisher.
7. Five. [Desert, Red-rumped, Mourning, Hooded and White-crowned Black.]
8. 1988 [9/9/88.]
9. Two. [Still two in 2004 – Lakes Bardawil and Burullus.]
10. Lake Idku.
11. Pygmy Falcon *Poliohierax semitorquatus* from mummified remains.
12. Black Crowned Crane.
13. Wire-tailed Swallow, March 1995.
14. Blackbird.
15. Dunn's Lark.

16. Giza Zoo.
17. *Merops orientalis cleopatra* and *M. o. cyanophrys*.
18. It was in a tree. Streaked Weavers are only known to nest in reeds in Egypt. (Although they do nest in trees in India.)
19. Marbled Teal and White-eyed Gull. [This was the answer in 1996. Marbled Teal no longer breeds in Egypt, and White-eyed Gull has been demoted/promoted to Near Threatened. Lappet-faced Vulture has, however, been added to the Vulnerable category.]
20. Desert Eagle Owl.
21. Sherif Baha El Din.
22. Nowhere – it is extinct in Egypt.
23. Richard Meinertzhagen.
24. Rocks.
25. Senegal Thick-knee and Senegal Coucal.
26. Corncrake.
27. The underwing-coverts of Spotted Eagle are darker than the rest of the underwing, whereas in the Lesser Spotted Eagle the underwing-coverts are usually lighter than the rest of the underwing.

GENERAL KNOWLEDGE 1996

1. Arthur Ransome.
2. Blakiston's Fish Owl.
3. A.A.Milne. [The quotation finishes "Which is why a Pooh is poohing, In the sun."]
4. 1955.
5. 1) Possible breeding, 2) Probable breeding and 3) Proved (or confirmed) breeding.
6. Small or undersized.
7. Waldrapp.
8. Black, white and red.
9. Great Crested Grebe.
10. Pheasant.
11. Kiwi.
12. A bird with half male/half female plumage.
13. Two gallons (or 9,092 mls).
14. Emperor Penguin. (1.5%).
15. They lay clutches of 2 eggs.
16. One of Sandgrouse, Buttonquails, Mousebirds and Waxbills.
17. The more northerly breeding populations of a species migrate further south than the more southerly breeding populations. (i.e. they leap-frog over them).
18. Barn and Long-eared Owls.
19. Flycatcher or Shrike.
20. A type of nightjar (Nyctibiidae).
21. Bearded Tit.
22. It lives in groups of 12 [give or take 8.]
23. A lek or communal display area.
24. Preen gland.
25. Chaffinch *Fringilla coelebs*.
26. Robin Redbreast.

27. Meadowlarks.
28. Hispaniola [Haiti and Dominican Republic.]
29. Madagascar.
30. Calf of Man.
31. Isle of May.
33. Red Grouse.
33. Steller's Eider.
34. James Bond.
35. Huia.
36. Abbotsbury, Dorset.
37. Common Eider.
38. Ruff.
39. Precocial.
40. Swallows.
41. Merlin.
42. Green Sandpiper.
43. Baikal Teal.
44. Grey Heron.
45. Long-eared Owl.
46. Northern Wheatear.
47. Whimbrel.
48. Nightjar.
49. Great Crested Grebe.
50. Megapodes.
51. It drops bones from a height to break them, in order to get at the marrow.
52. Alpine Chough.
53. The Chicken (Red Junglefowl).
54. Owls.
55. Ancient wing.
56. The Mayans.
57. Congo Peafowl.
58. Kakapo.
59. Edward Lear.
60. Marbled Murrelet.
61. Dylan Thomas.
62. The Sparrow.
63. His bow and arrow.
64. Oilbird.
65. By the white head of the latter, as some Flying Steamer Ducks are flightless and some Flying Steamer Ducks can fly (after a fashion). [This was the answer in 1996, but, of course, male Flying Steamer Ducks have an almost white head in the breeding season. Perhaps the fact that Flying Steamer Ducks tend to move inland to breed, which Flightless Steamer Ducks do not, is more reliable.]
66. They all do.

ANSWERS 1997: SPECIALIST SUBJECTS
Conservation of Globally Threatened Species in Europe

1. The refusal of the British government to control Ruddy Ducks which are spreading to the continent and hybridising with White-headed Ducks. [This is no longer the case.]
2. Great Bustard, max. 18kg.
3. 10-20 pairs of Zino's Petrel. [This was the answer in 1997. The present known population is 45 pairs.]
4. Corncrake, in about 30 countries in Europe.
5. 4 or 3. [Fea's Petrel, Zino's Petrel, Steller's Eider and Audouin's Gull. However, Steller's Eider has now been reclassified as Lower Risk / Least Concern.]
6. 8. [Zino's Petrel, Long-toed or Madeira Laurel Pigeon or Azores Bullfinch (Portugal), Spanish Imperial Eagle, Dark-tailed Laurel Pigeon, White-tailed Laurel Pigeon and Blue Chaffinch (Spain), and Scottish Crossbill (UK).]
7. Near Tara, Western Siberia, in about 1924.
8. Canary Island Black Oystercatcher.
9. 500 hectares or 1250 acres – Azores Bullfinch.
10. Whether or not the numbers are declining by at least 20% per 10 years in Russia, where most occur.
11. 1,700 in 1996. [In 1999 the population was estimated at approx. 2,200.]
12. Only Spain. [It nested in Morocco in 1991 and in Portugal until 1977.]
13. The eastern side.
14. Hunting and egg collecting.
15. Graciosa.
16. Every 5 years.
17. Corncrake and Aquatic Warbler. [Since 1997, Greater Spotted Eagle has been added as Vulnerable and Ferruginous Duck, White-tailed Eagle and Great Snipe are considered as Near Threatened.]
18. To control the expansion of the exotic flora and promote the regeneration of the laurel forest.
19. Merdja Zerga.
20. Corncrake.
21. He does not feed the incubating female or young.
22. Great Bustard.
23. Steller's Eider. [See the answer to question 5 above.]
24. Duck (Russian).
25. White-headed Duck.
26. Human disturbance, including hunting.
27. Steller's Eider. [See the answer to question 5 again.]
28. Freira Conservation Project.
29. Competition from Yellow-legged Gulls.
30. Prussian.
31. Spanish Imperial Eagle.

Grey Geese of Britain and Europe

1. Lesser White-fronted Goose. [The entire Fennoscandian population gathers there (in Arctic Norway) prior to migration].
2. Sugar beet waste left in fields.
3. Lag is an old word for goose.
4. 1948. (Accept 1946-1950).
5. White-fronted Goose.
6. Slamannnan Plateau (Fannyside Farm), Lanarkshire and the Yare Valley, Norfolk.
7. Svalbard (Spitzbergen).
8. White-fronted Goose.
9. Pink.
10. Lesser Snow Goose *Anser c. caerulescens*. (Blue phase Greater Snow Goose *A. c. atlanticus* is extremely rare).
11. Bean Goose. [I wish that I knew what this question means. Ed.]
12. Greylag Goose. [Arguably. Ed.]
13. Its red feet – *erythropus* – red-footed.
14. 20,000-30,000. [The 1999-2000 population would appear to have been 27,438, but this figure is compromised by the uncertain origin of some birds.]
15. White-fronted Goose – from its call.
16. None.
17. Iceland.
18. Lesser White-fronted Goose.
19. Pink-footed Goose.
20. Bean Geese.
21. To protect the small native population of breeding Greylags in Scotland.
22. Good news.
23. Sir Peter Scott.
24. Humber Estuary.
25. A move to improved grassland.
26. 46-75. [In Jan 2004 the population was 52 birds, all wintering in the Evros Delta. This excludes birds from the reintroduction scheme.]
27. Pink-footed Goose 'winks' and Bean Goose 'hanks'.
28. Swan Goose – known in domestication as Chinese Goose.
29. 16 minutes per lb, or 40 minutes per kg. [It is amazing how many cookery books do not give this vital information, saying "cook for 2-3 hours according to size", or some equally unhelpful phrase. Ed.]

Birds of London 1960-1997

1. Walthamstow Reservoir.
2. Rook.
3. The late Rupert Hastings.
4. 40 sq miles – a rectangle of 5 miles N to S and 8 miles E to W.
5. American Golden Plover.
6. Shelduck.
7. 1988-94.
8. Herring Gull and Lesser Black-backed Gull.
9. Coal Tit.

10. Jackdaw and Tree Sparrow.
11. 1968. (Two pairs nested but no young were reared).
12. Charing Cross.
13. Black Redstart.
14. Jeffery Harrison and Peter Grant.
15. Regent's Park.
16. Brompton Cemetery, 1982.
17. Surrey Docks.
18. Grey Wagtail.
19. Cormorant.
20. Rose-ringed Parakeet.
21. Five. [Barn, Little, Tawny, Long-eared and Short-eared Owls.]
22. Common Nighthawk.
23. House Sparrow.
24. October.
25. Dartford Warbler.
26. Water Pipit.
27. Waxwing.

Birds of Texas

1. Golden-cheeked Warbler.
2. Burrowing Owl.
3. Sennett's. [I have had difficulty in confirming this answer, and cannot find any reference to this in print. If it is correct, it is confusing, as George Sennett, who collected extensively in Texas in the 19th century, has the southern Texas race of the Seaside Sparrow *Ammodromus maritimus sennetti* named after him. Olive Sparrow is sometimes referred to as Texas Sparrow, but Tex Ritter is hardly a Hollywood legend of yesteryear. Ed.]
4. Bronzed Cowbird.
5. Bewick's Wren.
6. Black-headed Oriole.
7. Neotropic (or Olivaceous Cormorant)...
8. Reddish.
9. Three. [Belted, Ringed and Green Kingfishers.]
10. False. If it turns up at all it is an extreme rarity.
11. Black-capped Vireo and Golden-cheeked Warbler.
12. High Island, of which the best known parts are Boy Scout Woods and Smith Oaks.
13. Roseate Spoonbill.
14. Tropical Parula – a US breeder confined to south Texas. The rest areas are the most reliable sites for finding them.
15. Eskimo Curlew.
16. Ivory-billed Woodpecker.
17. Whooping Crane.
18. The Blue List.
19. Bachman. The first was a hit for Bachman Turner Overdrive, (not to be confused with "You ain't heard nothing yet", which was a hit for Al Jolson in 1919), and the second which is the habitat of Bachman's Sparrow.
20. (Northern) Mockingbird.

GENERAL KNOWLEDGE 1997

1. Gannet.
2. Starlings.
3. Hawaii.
4. Carpal joint.
5. Hoatzin. [There are in fact other species with functional claws on their wings. Screamers have claws on the wings which are used by the males when fighting, and Finfoots use their claws to aid climbing in vegetation.]
6. Both are in the genus *Oenanthe*.
7. The Liver Birds.
8. Wood Pigeon [Scottish.]
9. South America.
10. New Zealand.
11. Hawaii.
12. Cape Clear.
13. Kakapo.
14. Social Weaver.
15. Sooty Tern.
16. American Woodcock.
17. Kittiwake.
18. Shrikes (Laniidae).
19. Australia.
20. The lores.
21. Storm Petrel.
22. Pink.
23. Mediterranean Gull *Larus melanocephalus*. [This question is a bit ambiguous. Black-headed Gull's scientific name is *Larus ridibundus* which would make it Laughing Gull. Laughing Gull's scientific name is *Larus atricilla* which means 'black-tailed'!]
24. Trumpets [the Trumpeter Swan is the New World's largest wild swan.]
25. It feeds on the blood of other live birds.
26. Coot Club.
27. North America.
28. Emu. (The 'Emu War' was abandoned when the birds "adopted guerrilla tactics and split into small units, rendering the use of military equipment uneconomic. The machine-gun unit withdrew after a month and emu-proof fences were erected around the wheat-growing country").
29. South-east Asia.
30. Hummingbirds.
31. Jurassic.
32. Bald Eagle.
33. Red-necked Phalarope.
34. Parrots.
35. Madagascar.
36. On the upper mandible. [Beak or bill is not specific enough.]
37. White-tailed Eagle.
38. Andean Condor.
39. Wren *Troglodytes troglodytes*.
40. Goldcrest and Firecrest.
41. Rossini.

42. Red Grouse – *Trichostrongylus* is a parasite of Red Grouse.
43. (South) Wales.
44. Aristophanes.
45. 6 – 3 on each foot, but no hallux or hind toe.
46. 1970.
47. Snowy Plover.
48. Odin.
49. Two on each foot.
50. Wagtails and pipits (Motacillidae).
51. Bermuda. [Which is where they breed.]
52. At the side of the throat/chin.
53. Swift. [In Scotland, apparently, the Yellowhammer is sometimes called the Devil Bird. Diablotin, which means Devil Bird, is also used instead of Black-capped Petrel and Audubon's Shearwater, as well as for the Oilbird or Guacharo.]
54. Ring-billed Gull.
55. Fulmar.
56. Charlie Parker.
57. 1967.
58. Islay.
59. Nightjars.
60. Dark Chanting Goshawk.
61. A Wren.
62. Tring Reservoirs.
63. "One leg of a lark is worth the whole body of a kite", apparently.
64. Madagascar.
65. Spring.
66. Herpetology [Snake Bird, Crocodile Bird, Lizard Buzzard and Frogmouths]

ANSWERS 1998: SPECIALIST SUBJECTS
Ringing

1. Robin Sellers.
2. Rock Pipit, with 24,208.
3. 6 years, 11 months and 24 days.
4. 10 km.
5. 25,775,697. (Accept 24,775,697-26,775,697.) [31,086,165 by the end of 2002.]
6. £23.50. (Accept £23-£24.) [1998 prices, remember - it is now £28.50.]
7. By cloacal examination.
8. They all take different ring sizes for the two sexes.
9. It is not possible, as both adults and juveniles have complete moults at the end of the summer.
10. Ducks.
11. 1965.
12. H. F. Witherby and A. Landsborough Thomson.
13. Aberdeen University.
14. 1937.
15. The Permit system.
16. 1960s (1961).
17. EURING code 5.
18. Biblical quotations.
19. Nickel.
20. 1909.
21. Miss Elsie Leach.
22. Andy Gosler. [Currently Chris Du Feu.]
23. 2.0 mm.
24. 29 mm.
25. Blue Tit.
26. Swallow, Blackbird, Great Tit, Starling and Greenfinch.
27. Black-headed Gull.
28. 32 years and 30 days.

Birds of Gloucestershire

1. 1982.
2. Mandarin.
3. 1966 (accept 1964-1968).
4. 4.
5. 1945.
6. 420 (accept 410-430).
7. 1968.
8. Bewick's Swan.
9. Cotswold Water Park or Lechlade area.
10. One.
11. Ruddy Ducks escaping.
12. Ring-necked Duck - the first UK record, Slimbridge 1955.
13. Near Marshfield in June 1971.

14. N. J. Collar.
15. Moreton Valance.
16. Mellersh (*A Treatise on the Birds of Gloucestershire*, 1902).
17. Long-tailed Tit.
18. Woodchat Shrike.
19. The establishment of the Severn Wildfowl Trust at Slimbridge by Peter Scott.
20. Gyrfalcon.
21. Little Bustard.
22. Yellow-browed Warbler.

Names of British Birds

1. Goldeneye, Barrow's Goldeneye, Golden Eagle, Golden Pheasant, Golden Plover, Pacific Golden Plover, American Golden Plover, Golden Oriole and Golden-winged Warbler?
2. Yorkshire (Water Rail, Ring Ousel and Goosander).
3. Two - Brünnich's Guillemot and Rüppell's Warbler.
4. French – from 'gros bec', meaning 'thick bill'.
5. *Falco cherrug*.
6. Snow Bunting.
7. Yellow-billed Diver.
8. Pennant, 1776.
9. Black (30 species on the recent BOU list), followed by Red (28) and White(17).
10. Yellowhammers – old country names.
11. Nightjar.
12. Goldeneye.
13. Lapwing.
14. Swift.
15. Pied Flycatcher.
16. Manx Shearwater.
17. Sanderling.
18. Common and Arctic Terns.
19. Whinchat.
20. Great Grey Shrike.
21. Kittiwake.
22. Falcated Duck. [Falcated means sickle-shaped.]
23. Bonaparte's Gull *Larus philadelphia*.
24. Yellow-bellied Sapsucker. [As distinct from the Nightjar named for its liquid supper.]
25. Little Ringed Plover, now called Little Plover *Charadrius dubius*. [It seems to have missed out on the recent 'concessions' in British Birds.]
26. Ovenbird.
27. Great Knot.
28. Black Grouse.
29. Killdeer. [This is almost the last of the cringing puns.]
30. Gull, Sandgrouse, Grasshopper Warbler, Leaf Warbler and Bunting. [NB. Pallas's Rosefinch is NOT on the British List].
31. Ruff.
32. Avis = bird.
33. Flatarse.
34. Snorter.

Threatened Birds of the World

1. Slender-billed Curlew.
2. Pink Pigeon, Echo Parakeet, Mauritius Kestrel. [Although this was the official answer in 1998, other endangered species have benefited from conservation measures in Mauritius, whether classed as "projects" or not. The Critically Endangered Mauritius Fody has been aided by rat control and a captive rearing programme, and the Endangered Mauritius Olive White-eye has been helped by the rehabilitation of native vegetation. The Vulnerable Mauritius Cuckoo-shrike and Mauritius Bulbul have benefited from the creation of the Black River National Park and from rehabilitation of the native ecosystem in Conservation Management Areas.]
3. Kakapo.
4. Cape Verde Cane Warbler.
5. One. [Now none.]
6. Corncrake, Aquatic Warbler and Scottish Crossbill. [Scottish Crossbill is now classified as Data Deficient. White-tailed Eagle is also Near Threatened.]
7. 200-250. [In 2003 there were 91 nesting pairs.]
8. White-eyed River Martin. [*Pseudochelidon sirintarae* after Princess Sirindhorn Thepratanasuda.]
9. Three. [There have been none since 2001.]
10. South Korea, 1971. [Another debatable answer. There are considerable reservations on the reliability of this record, so the answer is probably in May 1964 on islands to the south of Vladivostok, Russia.]
11. WWT (The Wildfowl and Wetlands Trust).
12. Jerdon's Courser.
13. Kirtland's Warbler.
14. Hooded Plover. [This is now classified as Near Threatened.]
15. 19,000. [This answer was out of date in 1998, being a 1991 estimate. It was reckoned to be fewer than 10,000 in 1996 and is now 7,900-11,100.]
16. Tenerife, La Gomera and La Palma.
17. Russia, Poland, Belarus and Ukraine are the four main countries, with Hungary fifth.
18. Idaho. [This introduced population had dwindled to 1or 2 birds in 1999 and the reintroduction was discontinued. There is also a non-migratory reintroduced flock in Florida.]
19. White-breasted Thrasher and Martinique Oriole.
20. Ou.
21. Madagascar.
22. Rudd's Lark.
23. Mariana Crow and Guam Swiftlet.
24. Cracids (Cracidae).
25. Blue-billed Curassow – its generic and specific names are different. (NHC is *Pauxi pauxi*, AC is *Mitu mitu* and B-b C is *Crax alberti*).
26. Woodpecker (Picidae).
27. Amazon (Parrot). [Green-cheeked is also called Red-crowned.]
28. California Condor.

GENERAL KNOWLEDGE 1998

1. A male falcon.
2. Ravens.
3. The avian equivalent of the larynx.
4. Wren.
5. Quail.
6. Bee Hummingbird. [1.6 gms approx.]
7. Cuba.
8. Anagram of Pintado. [Painted in Portuguese.]
9. 905.
10. 8-16 kg.
11. Geese.
12. Feet.
13. Breast and belly.
14. Quail.
15. Two.
16. Egyptian Vulture.
17. After St Peter who walked on the water on the Lake of Gennesareth.
18. Onomatopoeic names.
19. 100-160kg.
20. Eagles.
21. Breast and throat (streaks).
22. Sandwich Tern.
23. An unusually flexible tibia-tarsal joint (ankle).
24. Eleanora's Falcon.
25. 4. [Accept 3-5.]
26. Pyriform. [Accept nothing less!]
27. Short toes.
28. Lapwings.
29. Chicken.
30. Approximately 4,000,000,000 apparently. [Accept 3,000 million-4,000 million.]
31. New Zealand.
32. A parrot.
33. Diomedes was a Greek warrior. Diomedes's dead companions were changed into seabirds.
34. They are all unclean and forbidden to be eaten.
35. A greatly enlarged crop or foregut.
36. Neck, breast and upperparts.
37. Swan.
38. A Bobolink.
39. 1874. [1842 unsuccessfully.]
40. Two.
41. A watch.
42. Lord Snowdon.
43. True.
44. Herons.
45. Red-billed Quelea.
46. Approximately 1,500,000,000 apparently. [Accept 1,000 million-2,000 million.]
47. A type of fig.

48. It dives from the air for its food.
49. *The Handbook of British Birds.*
50. 2.5-3.5 metres. [8 feet 3 inches - 11 feet 6 inches.]
51. Raven.
52. Wings.
53. Black and red.
54. Takahe.
55. Tawny Pipit.
56. A Greek prophetess/soothsayer.
57. Red.
58. Crows.
59. Coot. [Arguably. Capercaillie would also be an acceptable answer, although it is only the male which has an ivory-white bill.]
60. Berkeley Square.
61. A young pigeon.
62. A chattering.
63. James Fisher.
64. 34 years.
65. Contours, semiplumes, down, powder down, bristles and filoplumes.
66. 25 years.

ANSWERS 1999: SPECIALIST SUBJECTS
Birds of Australia

1. Brown.
2. Cairns.
3. Hoary-headed Grebe.
4. It is nocturnal – the Night Parrot.
5. Clamorous Reed Warbler. [Sometimes split as a separate species, Australian Reed Warbler.]
6. Blackbird.
7. Swift Parrot and Orange-bellied Parrot.
8. Richard's Pipit. [Recent taxonomic proposals would make this answer incorrect.]
9. In a termite mound.
10. Noisy Pitta.
11. Paradise Parrot. [It is considered to be extinct although 5 birds were claimed to have been seen in 1990.]
12. A large wader migration.
13. 2 or 14. ["Two – Emu and Cassowary" was the original answer, neglecting the fact that there are feral Ostriches in South Australia and 11 species of penguin have been recorded, one of which breeds.]
14. They were alleged to spread prickly pear.
15. Manx Shearwater, Arctic Tern and Common Tern.
16. Golden Bowerbird.
17. Satin Bowerbird.
18. Banded Stilts undergo mass migrations for mass breeding attempts only once every few years, when the rains fill up their salt lakes.
19. Australian Magpie.
20. Rifle birds.
21. Bassian, Eyrean and Torresian.
22. 6.
23. Forty-spotted Pardalote.
24. Innermost.
25. Great Crested Grebe, Great Cormorant, Little Egret, Osprey, Peregrine, Coot, Oystercatcher, Roseate Tern and Barn Owl.
26. Mallard, Feral Pigeon, Blackbird, Song Thrush, Skylark, Goldfinch, Greenfinch, House Sparrow, Tree Sparrow and Starling. ["Successfully" may not be the most felicitous adverb to have used in this question.]
27. Paradise Riflebird, Victoria's Riflebird, Magnificent Riflebird and Trumpet Manucode.
28. Orthonychidae.
29. They are the only representatives of their families to occur in Australia. [There are records of Pheasant-tailed Jacana of doubtful reliability.]
30. Red and blue.

Birds of Galapagos

1. 13.
2. Large, Medium, Small and Sharp-beaked Ground Finches, Common and Large Cactus Finches, Vegetarian Finch, Large, Medium and Small Tree Finches, Woodpecker Finch, Mangrove Finch and Warbler Finch.

3. Barn Owl and Short-eared Owl.
4. Blue-winged Teal, White-cheeked Pintail and Black-bellied Whistling Duck.
5. Medium Tree Finch.
6. Chatham Mockingbird.
7. Swallow-tailed Gull – the most nocturnal of all gulls.
8. Blue-footed Booby.
9. 13 (accept 12-14). [It all depends on what you mean by "main".]
10. Elliot's Storm-petrel.
11. Cape Douglas on Fernandina.
12. 150 miles approximately.
13. Black-footed, Laysan and Short-tailed Albatrosses.
14. *Thalassarche eremita* is the Chatham Albatross, and Chatham Island is another name for San Cristobal. [What a convoluted question and answer!]
15, 8 – Franklin's and Laughing Gulls, Royal, Common, Sooty and Black Terns and Pomarine and Arctic Skuas.
16, Black-billed Cuckoo.
17, Yellow Warbler.
18, It uses tools to extract insects from holes.
19, Espanola (Hood).
20. 6.
21. Charles Mockingbird only occurs on Champion and Gardner Islands.
22. 5.
23. There are two populations that breed at different times of year.
24. Papamoscas.
25. Up to 300 small pebbles.
26. They are an introduced species.
27. Masked Booby, Blue-footed Booby, Red-billed Tropicbird and Swallow-tailed Gull.

Birds of the Bailiwick of Guernsey

1. Citrine Wagtail.
2. Roderick Dobson.
3. Herm.
4. Jackdaw.
5. Robi Marsh.
6. Rose-breasted Grosbeak and Blackpoll Warbler.
7. Major-General Griff Caldwell.
8. Rich Austin.
9. Any colour you like.
10. Adrian Gidney.
11. C. C. Carey.
12. 1870s (1879).
13. Henry Le Marchant Brock.
14. 1900s (1903).
15. 1970 (accept 1965-1975).
16. Little Grebe.
17. Cory's Shearwater.
18. Little Egret.
19. Mallard.
20. Shelduck.

21. Common Crane.
22. Turnstone.
23. Three.
24. Les Etacq and Ortac.
25. Guernsey shoreline.
26. Madame Cholet (one of the Wombles of Wimbledon Common).
27. Eurasian Treecreeper.
28. Its scientific name is *Certhia familiaris*.
29. First-winter female.
30. Women, who can now inherit land on Alderney. [Not a terribly p.c. question, but more p.c. than the original law.]

Birds of Jordan

1. *Portrait of a Desert* by Guy Mountfort.
2. Marbled Teal and Lesser Kestrel. [Houbara Bustard, which was in the original answer, is now considered to be only Near Threatened (in its new Macqueen's guise), as is also the Syrian Serin.]
3. Blue Tit.
4. Brown Fish Owl.
5. Dr Bryan Nelson, author of the books *The Gannet*, *The Sulidae: Gannets and Boobies* and *Azraq: Desert Oasis*.
6. 1977.
7. House Crow.
8. Ostrich.
9. Tristram. (Tristram's (or Syrian) Serin and Tristram's Grackle are named after the Rev. H. B. Tristram, who wrote *The Land of Moab: travels and discovery on the east side of the Dead Sea and the Jordan* about his travels in 1873).
10. Black-headed Plover/Lapwing *Vanellus tectus*.
11. Sinai Rosefinch.
12. It was first described from a locality in Jordan.
13. The Kingdom of Moab is another name for Jordan.
14. Ian J. Andrews.
15. 374.
16. 150.
17. Ian J. Andrews, Fares Khoury and Hadoram Shirihai.
18. Aqaba sewage works.
19. Lesser Frigatebird.
20. 1st February.
21. Trumpeter Finch and Sinai Rosefinch.
22. Tristram's Grackle.
23. Rose-ringed Parakeet.
24. Arabian Babbler.
25. Syrian Serin.

GENERAL KNOWLEDGE 1999

1. Egyptian Goose.
2. Newcastle United.
3. Green Woodpecker.
4. Palm nuts/Fruit.
5. Horned Lark.
6. Seven. [Tree, Barn, Red-rumped and Cliff Swallows and Sand, Crag and House Martins.]
7. Grey Hen.
8. Peter Scott.
9. Labrador Duck.
10. Marmora's Warbler.
11. They were all believed to be extinct before being rediscovered.
12. The Albatross.
13. Giant.
14. Skua sp.
15. Unlucky. [It is a bird of ill omen in Norway, although a good omen in Sweden.]
16. Grey.
17. It nests on islands in the Nazca tectonic plate (Galapagos and Malpelo).
18. Sheffield Wednesday.
19. Ants.
20. Winter Wren.
21. Male.
22. 1991. [Accept 1989-1993.]
23. They were walking.
24. They are all known as Snotty.
25. Anton Chekhov.
26. *Portrait of a Desert* and *Portrait of a River*.
27. Desert Warbler.
28. Peacocks. ["Quinquireme of Nineveh from distant Ophir, Rowing home to haven in sunny Palestine, With a cargo of ivory, And apes and peacocks, Sandalwood, cedarwood and sweet white wine".]
29. Black.
30. (Florence) Nightingale.
31. Silk tail.
32. Little Auk.
33. Wrexham, Bristol City or Swindon Town.
34. Dipper.
35. Four. (European, Red-necked and Egyptian Nightjars and Common Nighthawk).
36. Northern Shrike.
37. Azores Bullfinch.
38. Madagascar Elephant-bird (*Aepyornis maximus*).
39. WZ or ZW.
40. Quark.
41. Henry Seebohm.
42. The Raven.
43. Connecticut, Kentucky, Louisiana and Tennessee.
44. Hawfinch.
45. *Cannabina* means 'Hemp' – one of its main foods.

46. Green.
47. Tristram's Warbler.
48. Black Guillemot.
49. Seven. [Chimney, Common, Pallid, Pacific, Alpine, Little and White-throated Needletail.]
50. Bank Swallow.
51. Bradford City.
52. Nuts (and seeds).
53. Parrots.
54. The Turkey (who lives on the hill).
55. Eurasian.
56. Eric Hosking.
57. Old Blue.
58. Garden Warbler.
59. Black Stilt [Maori name is 'kaki'.]
60. Puffin.
61. Golden.
62. She wrote the *Observer's Book of British Birds*.
63. Ravens.
64. Ethiopia.
65. Bastard wing.
66. Congo Peacock.

ANSWERS 2000: SPECIALIST SUBJECTS
Birds of Suffolk

1. 1947.
2. Bittern.
3. Churchill Babington.
4. Eskimo Curlew.
5. (Greater) Scaup.
6. 1930s (1932).
7. Spoonbill.
8. Meinertzhagen described this subspecies in 1939, naming it *billypayni*. Unfortunately, the race had already been described in 1925 under the more prosaic epithet *maroccanus*.
9. Minsmere, 14-15 August 1970.
10. 54 pairs in 1994.
11. Bittern.
12. 1882.
13. 66 on 27 February 1996.
14. Lark Sparrow.
15. Oriental Pratincole.
16. *Bledgrave Hall* (also published in North America under the title *The Awl Birds*).
17. Houbara Bustard at Hinton near Westleton in 1962. [This has now been specifically identified as a Macqueen's Bustard following taxonomic revision.]
18. Geoff Welch (Minsmere's senior wardens).
19. Red-eyed Vireo.
20. Great Bustard.
21. Allen's Gallinule. [A second, also moribund, individual was found at Portland on 10 February 2002.]
22. Ipswich Sparrow *Passerculus sandwichensis princeps*.
23. Black-winged Pratincole.
24. Golden Oriole.
25. David Bakewell.
26. Both were in the summer of 1862.
27. "I went to Blaydon Races, 'twas on the ninth of June, eighteen hundred and sixty-two on a summer's afternoon......"
28. 1882, near Thorpeness.

Birds of Morocco

1. Douyet, June 1993.
2. Meski.
3. 1991
4. 1991.
5. 40.
6. Double-spurred Francolin.
7. The black eyemask extends down over the chin and throat.
8. 14 species (accept 13 or 15): Bar-tailed Desert, Desert, Hoopoe, Dupont's, Thick-billed, Calandra, Short-toed, Lesser Short-toed, Crested, Thekla, Wood, Sky,

Shore (Horned), Temminck's Horned.
9. They are the cafes below Erg Chebbi north of Merzouga, well known to birders searching for Desert Sparrow.
10. Helmeted Guineafowl.
11. Bald Ibis.
12. Moussier's Redstart (after Jean Moussier).
13. They are sub-Saharan species with relict populations in Morocco.
14. 1985.
15. OUARZAZATE.
16. Glaucous-winged Gull.
17. Spur-winged Goose.
18. *subpersonata*.
19. 7 (accept 6 or 8): Northern (Seebohm's), Black-eared, Desert, Red-rumped, Mourning, White-crowned Black, Black.
20. Crimson-winged Finch.
21. True.
22. Levaillant's Green Woodpecker.
23. Houbara Bustard.
24. Brown-throated or Plain Martin.
25. Dark Chanting Goshawk.
26. (Northern) Goshawk and Red Kite.
27. *aliena*.
28. White-rumped Swift.
29. Mike Alibone.
30. It was the Moroccan Army's main parade ground.
31. They drove off like a bat out of hell. What did you expect them to do?
32. As a wintering site for Slender-billed Curlew.

British Rarities of the 1980s

1. A Scops Owl was present May-July 1980.
2. A Trumpeter Finch at Church Norton.
3. Egyptian Nightjar.
4. Lark Sparrow.
5. A male Black-eared Wheatear.
6. Calf of Man.
7. Marmora's Warbler - First for Britain, May-July 1982.
8. 37.
9. All had resident or long-staying Black Ducks, paired with local Mallards.
10. 1984 (last seen on 12th August).
11. Little Bustard.
12. Black-winged Stilt.
13. Cream-coloured Courser.
14. Great Knot.
15. Hudsonian Godwit in 1981 and Red-necked Stint in 1986.
16. Little Whimbrel (Sker, Glamorgan, 1982; Blakeney, Cley and Salthouse, Norfolk, 1985).
17. Varied Thrush.
18. Red-breasted Nuthatch at Holkham, Norfolk from 13 October 1989 to 6 May 1990 (206 days).

19. Green Heron and Great White Egret.
20. Ditchford Gravel Pits, Northamptonshire.
21. 1984.
22. Pacific Swift.
23. Cliff Swallow 1983. Crag Martin 1988. (Not Tree Swallow = 1990).
24. Two, both on Scilly in 1984 and 1985.
25. Grey-tailed Tattler in October/November 1981.
26. Britain's first Rock Sparrow.
27. Pied-billed Grebe and Ivory Gull.
28. Little Crake at Cuckmere Haven; and Sora at Pagham Lagoon.
29. Collared Pratincole. [It was in fact an Oriental Pratincole.]
30. Cedar Waxwing and Brown-headed Cowbird.

Bedfordshire's Birds

1. Hobby.
2. Two.
3. Bill Oddie.
4. Oystercatcher.
5. Shags. (There was a flock of 20-30!).
6. Common Buzzard.
7. Magpie.
8. Tree Sparrow.
9. Vauxhall. (They bred at Vauxhall's factory in Luton).
10. Dipper.
11. Cetti's Warbler.
12. Flitwick Moor (pronounced Flittick Moor).
13. Mandarin Duck.
14. April.
15. Blunham Gravel-pit or Blunham Lake.
16. Barred Warbler.
17. Red-backed Shrike.
18. Linnet.
19. 1971.
20. Lady Amherst's Pheasant.
21. Bluethroat.
22. Pectoral Sandpiper, Baird's Sandpiper, Wilson's Phalarope and American Golden Plover.
23. Thirty-five.
24. Gadwall.
25. Razorbill.
26. Long-tailed Skua.
27. Spoonbill.
28. Dartford Warbler.
29. Peregrine.
30. Blows Downs or Dunstable Downs.

GENERAL KNOWLEDGE 2000

1. Mistle Thrush.
2. 1933.
3. Quail.
4. Head (crown and nape), wings and tail.
5. Snakes / Reptiles.
6. 1994.
7. Wallace's Standardwing.
8. A Caribbean frog.
9. Buff-browed Cliffcreeper.
10. The female has a white iris (the male has a black iris).
11. A Sheathbill.
12. 1975.
13. Wandering Albatross.
14. *The Lark Ascending*.
15. Gannet.
16. Passenger Pigeon.
17. In a bird's egg.
18. Common Bulbul.
19. Sacred Ibis.
20. Song Thrush.
21. The 39th Foot, later 1st Battalion Dorset Regiment, later the Devonshire and Dorset Regiment. [A Regiment will suffice!]
22. Wing coverts.
23. LBJ. [= little brown job.]
24. Hyraxes.
25. Green-winged Compost-maker.
26. 1992.
27. Great Bustard.
28. Gadwall.
29. (Thieving) Magpie.
30. The male has a broader black ventral stripe.
31. Leaf watcher.
32. 1858.
33. Wishbone or clavicles.
34. A band on the wings.
35. Giant Petrel.
36. 1996.
37. 1993.
38. Yellowhammer.
39. Plain Woodhaunter.
40. A fish (bummalo).
41. 1996.
42. Vietnamese Pheasant.
43. The female has an orange lower mandible.
44. (Apple) Snails.
45. Yellow-eared Parrot *Ognorhynchus icterotis*.
46. Royal.
47. Blackbird.

48. Carolina Parakeet.
49. A tern.
50. Swan Lake.
51. Turacos.
52. Albatross. [Specifically, one of the group of smaller albatrosses.]
53. 1999.
54. Seven-coloured Tanager.
55. At the top of the frontal shield. [If you are lucky.]
56. Purple Martin.
57. 1994.
58. Red-eyed Dove.
59. Blue-throated Prickletail.
60. A piece of paper. [28.75 inches by 42 inches.]
61. 251. [Give or take 10.]
62. The male has a red centre to the black malar stripe.
63. The Nutcracker Suite.
64. Bones.
65. Portugal.
66. Badger

ANSWERS 2001: SPECIALIST SUBJECTS
Twitching in the UK 1985-1995

1. Little Whimbrel/Little Curlew, seen between Blakeney and Salthouse from 24 August to 3 September 1985.
2. Shetland – Noss, in June 1985.
3. 1971, when one was seen at Dungeness, Minsmere and Dungeness again, between July and September.
4. 1987.
5. 1988 at Dinas Head.
6. To see a Swinhoe's Petrel trapped during tape-luring sessions.
7. Female Harlequin Duck *Histrionicus histrionicus*.
8. Great Bustards.
9. Rüppell's Warbler.
10. A first-winter Red-flanked Bluetail spent from 30 October – 8 November 1993 there.
11. Tresco, Scilly.
12. Yellow-throated Vireo.
13. Black-faced Bunting – a first-winter male trapped on 8 March stayed to 24 April.
14. Caspian Plover, last recorded on almost the same day in 1890 (22nd May).
15. 38 – (Accept 5 each way, 33-43). (The list stood at a round 550 at the end of 1995).
16. Pied Wheatear.
17. Stone Creek.
18. Bay-breasted Warbler.
19. Blue-cheeked Bee-eater – at least one twitcher saw both these birds on the same day!
20. Two answers needed: Golden-winged Warbler at Larkfield, near Maidstone, and Red-breasted Nuthatch in Holkham Pines.
21. Pacific Golden Plover.
22. St Kilda.
23. Grey-cheeked Thrush at Slimbridge (in October) and Yellow-billed Cuckoo at Sandy (in December).
24. (20 September) 1995 on Fetlar, Shetland.
25. Wilson's Warbler.
26. Pallas's Sandgrouse.
27. Ganga de Pallas.
28. 15 September 1989.
29. Spectacled Warbler at North Cliff Country Park, Filey and Greater Yellowlegs at the Ouse Washes.
30. Flamborough.

British Seabirds

1. Traditional harvesting of seabird eggs from Yorkshire cliffs by men lowering themselves on ropes.
2. 1844.
3. Fulmar.
4. (European) Storm-Petrel.

5. Sule Sgeir. (A guga is a young Gannet).
6. 1967.
7. *Oceanodroma leucorhoa*.
8. It derives form the same root as 'goose'.
9. 1784. [Described in 1787.]
10. 40-51 days (average 44 days).
11. Little Auk.
12. 16.
13. Apparently occupied territory.
14. Inaccessible Island, Nightingale Island and Gough Island.
15. Inaccessible Island, Nightingale Island and Gough Island.
16. Firth of Forth.
17. St Kilda.
18. 1968.
19. 340-500 grams. [A Tystie is a Black Guillemot.].
20. 90%.
21. The Monach Islands.
22. Foula.
23. False.
24. 2,600.
25. Gazza marina.
26. Arctic Skua and Arctic Tern.
27. Second decade of the 19th Century (1813).
28. 1948.

Terns of Europe

1. Black Tern.
2. The Azores (a few pairs are regular).
3. Roseate Tern *Sterna dougallii*.
4. Royal Tern or Sandwich Tern or Forster's Tern.
5. Caspian Tern. [NB. Royal Tern is misleadingly named *Sterna maxima*.]
6. Whiskered – Black – White-winged Black.
7. Because Aleutian Tern had never been recorded anywhere in North America other than Alaska, and wasn't until 1985.
8. 8,000km.
9. August 1974.
10. 18-20 days.
11. Arctic Tern.
12. 0.
13. 6.4-7.2cm.
14. *Gelochelidon nilotica*.
15. Bridled Tern.
16. 5 (Gull-billed, Caspian, Lesser Crested, Sandwich, Black).
17. A loud far carrying Grey Heron-like "*Kraaa*".
18. Inca Tern (escaped birds).
19. Carlsberg.
20. 17cm.
21. Caspian Tern.
22. Sandwich Tern.

23. Fraticello.
24. Pacific coast between California and Central America.
25. Mediterranean.
26. A laughing swallow.

Birds of the Estuaries of North-West England

1. Bar-tailed Godwit.
2. Spain.
3. 29,955.
4. Barnacle Goose.
5. 1972.
6. Yes.
7. 3,278.
8. Dunlin (mean of 31,262 between 1994 and 1999, whilst Knot's mean over the same period was 26,648).
9. Winter 1997-98.
10. 5 (at the Dee Estuary).
11. Common Scoter.
12. 0.
13. 45,500 ha.
14. Dee Estuary.
15. Oystercatcher, Knot, Dunlin, Bar-tailed Godwit, Curlew, Redshank.
16. Oystercatcher, Knot, Dunlin, Bar-tailed Godwit, Curlew, Redshank.
17. 11. (Whooper Swan, Pink-footed Goose, Barnacle Goose, Shelduck, Pintail, Oystercatcher, Knot, Dunlin, Bar-tailed Godwit, Curlew and Redshank).
18. False.
19. 2. [3 now – Ribble, Dee and also Alt.]
20. Curlew.
21. 57.
22. Shelduck, Wigeon, Teal.
23. Duddon.
24. No.
25. Common and Little Terns.
26. Killdeer.
27. *Charadrius hiaticula.*

GENERAL KNOWLEDGE 2001

1. Mew Gull.
2. Treecreeper.
3. The type specimen was released alive.
4. Endangered.
5. Falkland Islands.
6. Extinct.
7. 1993.
8. Corncrake.

9. 2,680.
10. 381,795.
11. Longline fishering.
12. Hoho.
13. The Raven.
14. (Great) Bittern.
15. John James Audubon.
16. The Sandpiper.
17. Nil.
18. Red Phalarope.
19. Foot and Mouth Disease.
20. Robert Gillmor.
21. Mauritius.
22. 5,317.
23. Bachman's Warbler.
24. Stanley Cramp.
25. The adult and juvenile plumage are hardly separable.
26. Drab Flycatcher.
27. Linnet's.
28. 1991.
29. Red-breasted Goose.
30. They are all members of monospecific families.
31. Diablotin / Devil Bird.
32. Woodlark.
33. Waved Albatross.
34. Contours, semiplumes, down, powder down, bristles and filoplumes.
35. Parasitic Jaeger.
36. Pheasant.
37. It is the Ivory-billed Woodpecker – the flagship species for 2001.
38. Tim Appleton.
39. New Caledonia.
40. Black-spectacled Tanager. [But.... there is a Spectacled Tanager.]
41. The Hastings Rarities.
42. George Bristow.
43. 1997.
44. (Andean) Cock-of-the-Rock.
45. 940.
46. The type specimen was in a miserable state ['*infelix*' means 'unhappy' or 'miserable', the bill and the greater part of the tail having been shot away.]
47. The syrinx.
48. Light-mantled Sooty Albatross.
49. Dr Edward Wilson.
50. Roger Peterson, Guy Mountfort, P. A. D. Hollom.
51. Leks.
52. "My little Chickadee".
53. A Wren.
54. Hen Harrier.
55. Madeira.
56. 29. [Accept 23-35.]
57. Cuban Kite.
58. 2000.

59. Wandering Albatross.
60. (Nocturnal) Curassow.
61. Squalid Flycatcher.
62. Chestnut-eared Laughingthrush.
63. It's onomatopoeic.
64. Charles Tunnicliffe.
65. 7,182.
66. Leach's Storm-petrel.

ANSWERS 2002: SPECIALIST SUBJECTS
British and Irish Twitching 1980-1989

1. Grey-tailed Tattler, Little Whimbrel, Lesser Crested Tern and Moussier's Redstart.
2. American Coot.
3. Lesser Grey Shrike.
4. Marmora's Warbler.
5. Eleanora's Falcon.
6. Tristram's Storm-petrel. [NB. This record of Matsudaira's Storm-petrel was not accepted by the BBRC.]
7. There were two different individuals.
8. The first Savannah Sparrow for Britain and Ireland at Portland Bill (in Dorset) was racially identified as *princeps*, known as Ipswich Sparrow.
9. Forster's Tern.
10. Eleanora's Falcon.
11. Green Heron. (For the sake of argument accept Green-backed Heron).
12. October 1987 (found dead in Lothian).
13. Mourning Dove, Double-crested Cormorant, Great Knot, Red-breasted Nuthatch, Golden-winged Warbler and Swinhoe's Petrel.
14. 86 days. (Accept 80 – 90).
15. 1984.
16. Lesser Crested Tern on the Farne Islands.
17. Chestnut-sided Warbler and Wilson's Warbler.
18. Grey Catbird (1986).
19. Cape Clear.
20. Little Swift (moribund at Studland in November), and White-throated Needletail (at South Ronaldsay in June).
21. Stilt Sandpiper (18-25 August 1987) and Terek Sandpiper (12-13 June 1989).
22. 1987.
23. Little Whimbrel and Long-toed Stint.
24. Moussier's Redstart added and Siberian Rubythroat (from 1977) taken off.
25. Kessingland.
26. 1981 (Fair Isle).
27. Magnolia Warbler.

Birds of Southern Africa

1. Rudd's Lark.
2. Burchell's Courser (also accept Double-banded Courser).
3. Burchell's Starling, Burchell's Sandgrouse and Burchell's Courser.
4. Namibia.
5. Blue-billed Firefinch.
6. Orange-breasted, Neergaard's, Greater Double-collared, Southern or Lesser Double-collared.
7. Fork-tailed Drongo.
8. They were Jackass Penguins fitted with satellite transmitters that swam back from Port Elizabeth to Dassen and Robben Islands after a catastrophic oil spill from the sinking of the ship *Treasure*.

9. Chaffinch.
10. Pin-tailed Whydah.
11. Hamerkop.
12. Swaziland. (It never bred in Zimbabwe, and is almost extinct in Namibia and Mozambique).
13. Yellow White-eye.
14. Ostrich.
15. St Croix (near Port Elizabeth).
16. 6. (Ostrich, Jackass Penguin and 4 vagrant penguins: (King, Gentoo, Macaroni and Rockhopper).
17. Black Coucal.
18. Mocking Chat (Cliff Chat).
19. One (African Broadbill).
20. Little Blue Heron.
21. Dickinson's Kestrel, Wahlberg's Eagle, Montagu's Harrier, Ayres' Hawk Eagle. (Could also accept Verreaux's Eagle, generally known as Black Eagle in southern Africa).
22. Zimbabwe.
23. Sacred, Hadada, Southern Bald and Glossy.
24. Chatham Albatross.
25. Pennant-winged Nightjar (only the female incubates).
26. Dickinson's Kestrel. (Accept Grey Kestrel also).
27. Thick-billed Lark.
28. Greater Frigatebird.
29. Strandfontein.
30. Striped Kingfisher.

British Bird Songs and Calls

1. "A little bit of bread and no cheese".
2. Extensive use of mimicry in their songs.
3. Snipe, Ruddy Duck, Lapwing, Mute Swan. [There are quite a few other possible answers, e.g. wing-clapping by Woodpigeon and Nightjar, drumming by woodpeckers, bill-snapping by owls, for starters.]
4. Cuckoo, Curlew, Chiffchaff, Kittiwake, Peewit and Twite [not Hoopoe!]
5. Corn Bunting.
6. John Keats.
7. Penduline Tit.
8. Great Tit.
9. Gilbert White.
10. Hobby.
11. Song Thrush.
12. Great Auk.
13. Nightingale.
14. Ludwig Koch.
15. Common Crane.
16. Corncrake *crex* and Turtle Dove *turtur*.
17. Skylark [*The Lark Ascending*.]
18. River Warbler.
19. Whimbrel.
20. Norfolk or Suffolk [Golden Oriole.]

21. Sussex, 1955.
22. Collared Dove.
23. Black Grouse, Capercaillie and Ruff.
24. (Has to include the cork out of the bottle pop at the end!)
25. Song Thrush.
26. Cape May Warbler.
27. Woodcock.
28. Avocet.
29. It is disyllabic ('hoo-eet'), not monosyllabic ('hueet').
30. 'Pee pee pee…' [i.e. 3 or 4 'pee' notes.]

Birds of Cuba

1. 132. [Allow 128-136.]
2. 16. [Allow 14-18.]
3. Johannes Gundlach.
4. Antillean Nighthawk *Chordeiles gundlachii*, Bahama Mockingbird *Mimus gundlachii*, Cuban Vireo *Vireo gundlachii*.
5. Eurasian Collared Dove.
6. Cuban Woodpecker.
7. Cuban Macaw.
8. Ovenbird.
9. Martin Davies.
10. Bunting.
11. It is the smallest known species of bird in the world - the Bee Hummingbird.
12. 1.9 grams.
13. 1987.
14. The Cuban Trogon, because it is coloured red, white and blue, the colours of the national flag [a bit fanciful – it has as much green as blue, which does not feature in the flag.]
15. Cayo Paredon Grande [there have also been some claimed sightings from neighbouring Cayo Coco.]
16. Peregrine Falcon, Merlin and Osprey. [Also accept Northern Harrier, which is often considered conspecific with Hen Harrier.]
17. Oriente Warbler and Yellow-headed Warbler.
18. Despite being named after the country, none is endemic to Cuba.
19. 18.
20. 1962 and 1964 on Zapata peninsula.
21. Townsend's Warbler. It has never been recorded in Cuba.
22. Cuban Solitaire.
23. Bicknell's Thrush.
24. White-tailed Tropicbird. It is the only one to be found in the eastern part of Cuba.
25. The Cuban Gnatcatcher has a black auricular crescent, running from behind its eye, whereas the Blue-gray Gnatcatcher has no black facial markings in its winter plumage (and a black eyebrow in its breeding plumage).

GENERAL KNOWLEDGE 2002

1. Bullfinch.
2. Cretzschmar's Bunting.
3. Red-brown.
4. 1984. (Also accept 1985).
5. 3.
6. 2001.
7. Ivory-billed Woodpecker.
8. Great Auk.
9. (Three-wattled) Bellbird.
10. It was the first prison sentence for offences relating to egg-collecting under the Countryside and Rights of Way Act.
11. Cambodia and Laos (formerly Vietnam and Thailand).
12. Purple-rumped Sunreader.
13. Albatross. (Golden Eagle is also acceptable).
14. Slender-billed Curlew.
15. Goldfinch.
16. Güldenstädt's Redstart.
17. Black.
18. 1994.
19. House Sparrow.
20. 30,000. (31,717 actually).
21. 1995.
22. Slender-billed Curlew, Audouin's Gull, Marbled Teal, Greater Flamingo.
23. Roger Tidman.
24. Bombay Duck.
25. (Black-backed) Forktail.
26. Fork-tailed Drongo.
27. Wrens.
28. Five. [Green, Great Spotted, Lesser Spotted Woodpeckers, Wryneck and Yellow-bellied Sapsucker.]
29. Rose-ringed Parakeet, Alexandrine Parakeet, Monk Parakeet, Blue-crowned Parakeet and Budgerigar.
30. Chaffinch.
31. Phainopepla.
32. Brown/Vinaceous red-brown.
33. 1978.
34. To prevent preening after oil-spills (and to keep them warm).
35. Blue-breasted Starlet.
36. Corsican Nuthatch, Sardinian Warbler, Cyprus Warbler, Cyprus Pied Wheatear, Balearic Shearwater, Corsican Finch (recently split from Citril Finch).
37. 1997.
38. (Andean) Cock of the Rock.
39. Egyptian Plover.
40. 1992.
41. Macaroni.
42. (Rock) Hyraxes.
43. Bald Ibis.
44. Nightjar.

45. White.
46. Hawfinch.
47. Dickcissel.
48. Green.
49. 1994.
50. Bald Ibis.
51. *Rusty Flies South*.
52. 1992.
53. White-moustached Hermit.
54. Common Dormouse.
55. (Black-bellied) Sandgrouse.
56. 59lbs 2oz. (27kg).
57. James Fisher.
58. 12oz (350gm).
59. 1989.
60. £3,000.
61. Rook.
62. Corncrake. (Accept Buff-banded Rail also).
63. Grasshopper Warbler. [Accept Savi's also.]
64. White-backed, Long-billed and Slender-billed Vultures. [This is almost certainly as a result of poisoning by Diclofenac].
65. Light-mantled Sooty Albatross.
66. 33. [Accept 31-35.]

ANSWERS 2003: SPECIALIST SUBJECTS
Birds of the Dominican Republic

1. None - the 26 Hispaniolan endemics are all found in Haiti as well as the Dominican Republic.
2. A. S. Dod.
3. Black-crowned Palm-Tanager *Phaenicophilus palmarum* and Gray-crowned Palm-Tanager *P. poliocephalus*.
4. Black-capped Petrel *Pterodroma hasitata* and Audubon's Shearwater *Puffinus lherminieri*.
5. Hispaniolan Trogon *Priotelus roseigaster*. (It is also known there as 'Red Knickers' Calecon rouge).
6. Chapman's Ground Warbler *Xenoligea montana*.
7. *Tyto ostologa*, the Giant Owl.
8. Grey Kingbird.
9. Rufous-collared Sparrow.
10. Palmchat - it is the one bird family endemic to Hispaniola.
11. At the base of the neck feathers - not visible in the field.
12. La Selle Thrush.
13. Hispaniolan Parakeet.
14. Hispaniolan Emerald.
15. Antillean Mango *Anthracothorax dominicus* and Vervain Hummingbird *Mellisuga minima,* and occasional Ruby-throated Hummingbird *Archilocus colubris*.
16. Brown Pelican *Pelecanus occidentalis*. [The somewhat larger American White Pelican may occur as a vagrant, as may the Tundra Swan, but neither is found 'regularly'.]
17. *Leucometopia*. [*Geotrygon caniceps leucometopia*.]
18. The wing [the male has white notches on the primaries and a barred wing-panel.]
19. Hispaniolan Crossbill. [Generally considered to be a race of White-winged or Two-barred Crossbill *Loxia leucoptera megaplaga*.]
20. Ridgway's Hawk (Critically Endangered).
21. Red Junglefowl.
22. William Beebe.
23. Flat-billed Vireo *Vireo nanus*.
24. Bay-breasted Cuckoo.
25. Nutmeg Mannikin (Scaly-breasted Munia) *Lonchura punctulata* and Chestnut Mannikin *L. malacca*.
26. April 1996.(Accept 1995 & 1997).
27. Ridgway's Hawk.
28. Ashy-faced Owl.
29. Green-winged Teal.

Endemic Bird Families of Africa

1. Smallness. Apart from those of parasitic finches and cuckoos, they are the smallest of all birds in relation to body size.
2. Mansfield Parkyn.
3. Short-legged Ground-roller in Malagasy.

4. It does. (In Mole NP in Ghana).
5. Magpie *Pica* and New World vulture *Cathartes* = *Picathartes*.
6. Four - Ostrich, Shoebill, Hamerkop and Secretary Bird.
7. Helmeted Guineafowl. [Crested sometimes uses the same site repeatedly, but not really 'traditionally'.]
8. White-breasted Guineafowl.
9. Turacin (red) and turacoverdin (green).
10. Balaenicipitidae.
11. Blue Vanga.
12. Hamerkop.
13. Ostrich [used to nest in the Middle East - but not now.]
14. 95 days. [Accept 90-100.]
15. Short-legged Ground-roller.
16. Ambatovaky.
17. Pectinated middle toe.
18. From the Arabic for hunter bird (saqr-et-tair).
19. Four. Knysna (South Africa), Bannerman's (Cameroon), Red-crested (Angola) and Prince Ruspoli's (Ethiopia).
20. Neither, they are both about 38 cm in length.
21. 30 (according to Clements). [Accept 25-32, as there is some taxonomic disagreement, e.g. Howard and Moore give 28 and Wells 32.]
22. Four and two respectively.
23. Black-billed and Violet. [In 1901.]
24. Tauracinae.
25. Monocrotophos.
26. Ross's [Ross's Turaco, Ross's Gull, Ross's Goose.]
27. Cuckoo-roller (Courol).
28. 1833 [accept 1828-1838]
29. Dodo, Réunion Solitaire, Rodrigues Solitaire.
30. Gurney's Sugarbird (after John Gurney)
31. From the Latin *ratis*, a raft, referring to the fact that the skeleton has no keel.

Birds of New Zealand

1. It exterminated the entire population of a previously undescribed species of wren. [Circa 1890.]
2. Right.
3. The Chatham Island Taiko [Magenta Petrel.]
4. David Crockett.
5. Black-billed Gull.
6. There is a biased sex ratio – 28 of the birds are males who can't keep it in their trousers.
7. All pure-bred Black Stilts are ringed (banded).
8. Codfish Island.
9. Toroa Head, a headland near Dunedin, has the only 'mainland' albatross breeding colony (mainly Southern Royals, but also a few Northern Royal Albatrosses). The Maori name for the great albatrosses is Toroa.
10. Watching a Blue Duck.
11. Old Blue.
12. The last known Fiordland male Kakapo. [Accept oldest or 'most famous'.]

13. Brown Rats – the island had the highest population density of rats in the world.
14. Maori name for New Zealand Pigeon.
15. Bill-tip colour - green in Southern, red/brown in Northern.
16. Snares Island.
17. Bush Wren.
18. Four - Piopio, Huia, Bush Wren and Laughing Owl. [The Auckland Island Merganser became extinct in 1902 but this didn't live on the mainland.]
19. Neither, although they both breed on islands in the Chatham Islands group. Chatham Albatross breeds on Pyramid Rock, and Chatham Petrel breeds on South East Island or Rangitira Island.
20. Yellow-eyed, Fiordland Crested, Snares Crested and Erect Crested Penguins.
21. Collecting 30 birds for museum specimens at the turn of the 20th Century.
22. Yellow-eyed Penguin. [Black-browed Albatross - 3 kg; Yellow-eyed Penguin male - 5.5kg; female - 5.25kg.]
23. Auckland Islands Teal, Campbell Islands Teal, Brown Teal. They are all threatened.
24. Orange.
25. 1999.
26. 1,200-1,800m above sea level in the Seaward Kaikoura Mountains.
27. A Stitchbird.
28. South Island.
29. Piopio - the last New Zealand Thrush.
30. Red-legged Shag *Phalacrocorax gaimardi*, found along the west coast of South America.

Threatened Birds of Asia

1. 1964 [accept 1962 – 66.]
2. White-eyed River Martin *Pseudochelidon sirintarae*.
3. Kazakhstan, Russia, Mongolia, China.
4. Dusky Friarbird *Philemon fuscicapillus*. The mimic species is Dusky-brown Oriole *Oriolus phaeochromus*.
5. Rufous-headed Robin *Luscinia ruficeps*.
6. Narcondam Hornbill *Aceros narcondami*.
7. The Philippines.
8. Boana, Indonesia.
9. Seeding bamboo.
10. It is found in Isabela Province.
11. Grey-hooded and Rusty-throated.
12. Okinawa Rail. [Discovered in 1978 and described in 1981.]
13. It's from the Ancient Greek – Tragos = goat, Pan = the god Pan. [It presumably refers to the bare fleshy erectile horns that Tragopans have, arguably resembling those of the god Pan]
14. Negros Fruit-dove. A female collected in 1953.
15. Vietnam.
16. Snowy-cheeked and White-speckled.
17. Nine.
18. Palawan, Sulu, Mindoro Tarictic, Visayan Tarictic, Rufous-necked, Visayan Wrinkled, Narcondam, Sumba and Plain-pouched.
19. Steller's Sea-eagle.
20. Salvadori's. In all the others the person for whom they were named in English is

reflected in the scientific specific name but Salvadori's is *inornata*. Others are *bulweri*, *reevesii*, *humiae* and *ellioti*.

21. Nilgiri Woodpigeon *Columba elphinstoni*, White-bellied Shortwing *Brachypteryx major*, Broad-tailed Grassbird *Schoenicola platyura*, Rufous-breasted Laughingthrush *Garrulax cachinnans*.
22. See 21 above.
23. Giant Scops Owl *Mimizuku gurneyi*. [The other species is of course Gurney's Pitta *Pitta gurneyi*.]
24. 7. [Schneider's, Graceful, Azure breasted, Whiskered, Gurney's, Fairy and Blue-headed.]
25. Buru, Indonesia.
26. Two. Izu Leaf Warbler and Izu Thrush.
27. Slaty-mantled Sparrowhawk (from Papua New Guinea), Imitator Sparrowhawk (from Papua New Guinea and the Solomon Islands), New Britain Sparrowhawk (from Papua New Guinea). [For interest, the fourth is Gundlach's Hawk from Cuba.]
28. Giant Ibis *Pseudibis gigantea*.
29. Rueck's Blue-Flycatcher
30. Southern Cassowary and Northern Cassowary.
31. Christmas Island Frigatebird *Fregata andrewsi*. [Using poisoned bait the Australian Government, Environment Australia and Monash University have reduced the population in some places from 70,000,000 ants/hectare to 420,000 ants/hectare – but it's still a lot of ants.]

GENERAL KNOWLEDGE 2003

1. Red.
2. Black-capped Kingfisher.
3. No.
4. Manx Shearwater.
5. Syria.
6. They are names of birdwatching hides.
7. Sakalava Rail and Slender-billed Flufftail.
8. Blackest Antbird.
9. To move the thighs sensuously.
10. House Sparrow or Northern Wheatear.
11. Northern Wheatear or House Sparrow.
12. Namaqua Dove.
13. The same.
14. European Bee-eater.
15. 121. [Accept 109-133.]
16. Sardinian Warbler.
17. Wood (Nuthatch).
18. Abbott's Booby, Christmas Island Frigatebird, C.I. Imperial Pigeon, C.I. Hawk Owl and C.I. White-eye.
19. Yellow.
20. Hedgehogs.
21. For ceremonial headdresses.
22. Iraq Babbler.
23. Teal.
24. Stonking Hummingbird.

25. Cow, goat and sheep dung (which contains a yellow carotenoid pigment called lutein).
26. Skylark.
27. Chris Knights.
28. The proposed Cliffe Airport. [Thankfully, the proposal has now been shelved.]
29. Black-billed Wood Dove.
30. "AB-ys-SINE......AB-ys-SINE". [These answers were deeply upsetting to one of the contestants, who was able to give the audience a much more realistic imitation of their calls! However, the questions were taken from an article in the *Bulletin of the African Bird Club* (10:43), on the Editorial Board of which the complaining contestant sat.]
31. Spix's Macaw.
32. Northern.
33. Fuertes's Parrot *Hapalopsitta fuertesi*. [Although there were possible sightings in 1989.]
34. The cat eradication programme.
35. Red.
36. A pen.
37. Central Europe. [Germany, Holland etc. – not UK.]
38. Mallard.
39. All three.
40. It is not parasitic.
41. Max Nicholson and Guy Mountfort.
42. Guy Mountfort and Max Nicholson.
43. Sword-billed Hermit.
44. Magpie.
45. African Mourning Dove.
46. JE pleu-eu-eu-eure.
47. Three. [Griffon 112 pairs, Black/Cinereous 12 pairs, Egyptian 2 pairs.]
48. The Korean Demilitarized Zone (DMZ).
49. Basra Reed Warbler.
50. Vulturine Parrot (*P. vulturina*). [Not to be confused with Pesquet's Parrot of New Guinea which is also sometimes known as Vulturine Parrot.]
51. Green.
52. He ended up in an Inuit deep-freeze. [One of six radio-tracked Brent Geese.]
53. 1947. [Accept 1942-1952. (They bred unsuccessfully in 1957).]
54. Goldeneye.
55. Oil spill from the *Prestige*.
56. Female.
57. A beard.
58. Madagascar Fish-eagle and Madagascar Serpent-eagle.
59. Madagascar Serpent-eagle and Madagascar Fish-eagle.
60. Moneychanger.
61. Red-eyed Dove.
62. "I AM a red-eyed-dove".
63. Vitamin C.
64. Kangaroo Parrot.
65. Ascension Frigatebird.
66. 44. [Accept 40-49.]

INDEX OF SPECIALIST SUBJECTS